THE TRUE

The Memory Series

"A Trilogy of Ghosts" is a composite of three books called THE TRUE.

Art Concept and Cover Design: Maria Miu

The book THE TRUE is a work of fiction/reality. Some names, characters, places, and incidents are a product of author imagination. Locations and public names are sometime used for atmospheric purposes. Any resemblance to actual people, living or dead, or to business, companies, institutions, or locales are sometimes coincidental.

CIP / National Library of Romania
KORNFELD, SARAH
THE TRUE / Sarah Kornfeld. - Bucharest : Integral, 2021
ISBN 978-606-992-641-3

821.111

Publisher: Costel POSTOLACHE
Developmental Editor: Sally ARTESEROS
Copy Editor: John MADERA
Layout and Graphic Design: Stelian BIGAN

ISBN 978-606-992-641-3

SARAH KORNFELD

THE TRUE

INTEGRAL

Content

In memory of Alexandru Darie Maximciuc
(1959-2019)

For Maria Miu

Prologue

When I learned that Diana Ross wanted to be in my movie, I wept. When I learned that Disney was to be the producer, I planned my retirement. When I was promised a one hundred million dollar budget, I knew my moment had come. And, there was the house in Bel Air. And then came the helicopter from Bob Iger, Disney's chairman–it was to arrive in the morning to take me to lunch in the executive suite so I could meet with Iger and Robert Chapek, Disney's CEO, to discuss the deal. It was dizzying.

But, let us start at the beginning, with the deeper search that led me to my brilliant Hollywood endeavors. In 2018, I learned that my once lover, now deep friend for over thirty years, was sick and possibly dying in Bucharest, Romania. He had been slowly, quietly drinking himself to death, and because

I lived far away, in California, I could only rely on the telephone for the truth.

"Baby, I'm great! I'm good…" Never pausing, never reflecting, he was always just fine, but disappearing, becoming a ghost.

"But, are you directing?" I would ask, wondering why he wouldn't let me see him on video anymore.

"Every day! I'm doing a new show, and it's going to be ferocious. Sixty people are in it. And it will be like being in a war", he said, firing up a cigarette, his inhalation long and dry.

"But, they tell me you are sick." I said.

"Who are *they*?"

(*They.)*

I should have stopped right there, I should have asked the harder question–who are "they" in this time of virtual lives? Who, indeed, was emailing me, pleading with me to come to Bucharest to make sure this man was safe? I did not know who *they* were, I just wanted to maintain the shared illusion that all was well.

But nothing was well. Trump with his corrupt soul was fomenting hate across America. Violence was wreaking havoc across my country once again;

and the people were taking to the streets. The days were slow, and we watched the news as if it were reality. It was a time of liars in a world of lies. *Nothing* was well.

"I told you Trump would win…" he said. "I told you it was coming."

"What's coming?" I asked.

"The lies", he said, quietly. "The worst of it… of government. I told you."

"Don't say that–"

"Why not? I lived through Ceaușescu, I lived through real nationalism. I can say it because I can see it–again."

He could see it, but I could not. And he was dying. Slowly. Painfully. Cirrhosis of the liver sucking him dry, he was no longer himself in 2018, but still young, with Eastern European film star looks, and Turkish and Jewish savoir faire, foregrounding the former but submerging the latter. Tall, with brown, Sephardic eyes, and pert mouth, he was the son of film stars in Communist Romania, once living a life of plenty in a place of hell. I'd met him in 1990 in London, and we had forged a connection that bobbed and weaved through all the changes in a "post-Communist" world. We had thought the world had changed, but over time, we saw nothing had and so we retreated to our respective countries.

Time took over. He stayed married and I got married. We had families and he ran a theater and directed the shows; and I wandered through the 2000s hoping to forget 1990 when I'd met him, when I was young and thought I'd discovered the world. So, his dying, this man of mine, this man who was not mine, confused me to the core. I texted him in waves of love and fear. I called to see what he needed from the West but he never responded. I made friends with Romanian actors online hoping they might tell me of his health: I was a machine of worry and isolation and none of this stopped his death. Ducu (his nickname) haunted me, though he was not yet dead.

Not yet dead–Ducu was a creative genius, a person of complex interests and fiery passions, global anxiety, professional power, and human insecurity. Rising from a country in ashes, he'd devoted himself to art, to life, to a life of art, an art of life. The heartache of the matter is that he was one of his generation's great romantic figures, his quixotic way perhaps precipitating his illness and death.

Existence was hard enough for many in Communist Romania, yet somehow *he* thrived. How to explain the resilience and creatively brilliance under constant repression? The light of discovery to chase away shadows? How did he do it: successfully break through from the margins in his own country? Why did he feel so lost when his heart was so authentic and real?

I write of his life with full understanding that I am not Romanian, yet I share the culture of a global theater world impacted by his loss. I am not a historian, yet I was present in the history of his arrival to an international scene. Ducu's life is a guide for a new generation of artists, a cautionary "how-to" for living an authentic, complex, and original life–a life where you can explore the farthest reaches of creativity, of wonder, of love.

On September 18, 2019, I received a text from a kind soul in Bucharest that my once lover, deep friend was gone. The online newspapers showed his funeral, people applauding his casket as they brought him to lie in state in his theater. There was the casket amid white candles placed upon the floor in the theater's lobby. There was Maria (his ex-wife but creative partner), slight and sad, holding the hand of a man who seemed to be keeping her feet on the ground. People sobbed in cafés. Artists cried beyond crying.

I sat alone in my room–there was nothing I could do. There was no one I could share this with.

I decided to lie to myself.

This was the moment. This was when it happened, when I turned off my senses and began a hunt for meaning to the end of his life–a meaning that can't really be validated, and would veer out of control. And, let me explain, many of the names in this story have been changed to protect people, though I will share some of the names of public figures for context. I have also chosen not to tell you about my child, or about "Anya"'s child, or the children brought into this story with the hope of convincing me of a larger story.

(*Just trust me.)*

It all starts with "Anya"–the lover of my lover, his caretaker at the end of his life, his angel, and soon to be mine.

ACT 1

"Follow me, reader! Who told you that there is no true, faithful, eternal love in this world! May the liar's vile tongue be cut out! Follow me, my reader, and me alone, and I will show you such a love!"

—Mikhail Bulgakov,
The Master and Margarita

Death on the Internet

I found myself so shocked by Ducu's death I pulled away from my friends and family and hid in my room. I could not talk about his death, I just felt it in my body. The only communication I was drawn to was on the Internet. Following the news of his death, I posted a picture of him on Facebook with some words. I felt that was real grief.

Anya had put up a photograph on her Facebook wall the same night Ducu died. It was a picture of the sky, the clouds streaked and the light fractured off buildings in Bucharest. The picture spoke to me immediately, reflected my thoughts exactly, the sky now less wondrous with him gone. I "liked" the photograph.

"Liking" a post I had up to celebrate Ducu's life, she posted images of Ducu's things in an apartment, and it hit me that perhaps these were images from a person who really knew him. You see, Ducu loved me, but Ducu loved many women–he had an enormous appetite for food, travel, sex, and romance. I'd known this for a long time. Having grown up in the theater, where I lived outside lines, loved deeply in profound ways, I didn't find it strange. Anya really could have a real connection to him, I'd thought, "liking" more of her photographs.

And then I got a text from her. Simple, sweet. She said she'd heard about me from Ducu. She knew he loved me. She would love to talk. We planned to use Facebook to talk one on one, and a few days after September 18th, 2019, I pulled my car to the side of the road to receive her call from Bucharest.

"Sarah?" Her voice was young, light, and very clear.

"Yes. Anya?"

"Yes, it's me. I'm so glad to hear your voice."

"Me, too. How are you?"

"Oh, you are kind, like Ducu said…"

"I don't know about that…"

"Yes, do you know he has died?"

"Yes. Were you…close?"

"Yes. Very."

"Were you…"

"I was his girlfriend."

I had not known he'd had a girlfriend. We had spoken on August 18th, my birthday, and he'd told me he'd been looking at a sunset in the mountains, that he wished he could share it with me–that he loved me. I shook my head. That was plausible, I'd told myself. I knew he could love me and love another…

"I'm so sorry for your loss", I said.

"And for you. He told me so much about you."

"He shared with you about New York?"

"Yes!"

"How we met in London?"

"Yes, at a theater?"

"Yes, the Royal Court Theater in 1990."

"Yes, yes, he told me."

"Anya, how the end was for him? I don't know anything about the last days of his life."

"He was very sick, you know, and he was very brave. He died alone. He was in a coma And they wouldn't let me see him…"

"Oh, that's terrible!"

"It was terrible. There were many people around him at the end. Mean people who tried to keep us apart, to own him…own his memory."

"Own his memory?"

"It's hard for an American to understand."

"Well, yes."

"But, I can try to explain it?"

"That would be so great, thank you!" "Can we speak later? I have a friend here who is driving me crazy and I need to see her out. In a few hours?"

"In a few hours", I said, Driving quickly home, I felt proud to have found someone real to talk with. But what had she meant about mean people? Why would that be? Why hadn't Ducu shared that with me? Good news in Romania was hard to come by, he'd say. But he'd made the theater he loved, told the stories he wanted to tell. What did Anya mean?

Driving on San Francisco's hills, over bumps and potholes toward the ocean I lived by, I thought of his body, his dead body. I tried not to think of Lars. I tried not to think about his hands, the calluses from working on the sailboats he'd built. I tried not to think about his brown eyes, kind, so kind I felt mean by comparison. Not an artist, but an artisan. I knew I had lost Lars because I wasn't brave enough to be loved.

Lars and I had tried for many years to be together. I'd met him through a friend from Hawaii; and Lars–tall, dark, and Scandinavian–had been the only man in years I had loved at first sight. We had fallen into each other easily, but things had always pulled us apart, not things, people, that is, Ducu, but also my confusion, the thought of having not seen that relationship through.

For years, I'd tried getting over Ducu, tried moving on, considering him a great memory, but I'd return, convulsively, circularly, to the scene of the crime, our relationship, webbed within guilt and longing.

Given the labyrinth I was in, I tried not to think about Lars that day, tried only to think of the dead–because that is where I'm most comfortable.

A few hours later, I sat on my bed drinking coffee. I propped up the pillows and felt alone. The past four years had been awful. Only a few days after Trump was elected, my parents were in an accident. The crash was as surprising as it was violent, my father immediately dragging himself out of the car toward my mother. Opening the door, he knew she was paralyzed. Rendered quadriplegic, she would spend the next few years learning to speak and eat, and attempt to walk.

One month after the accident, I was diagnosed with cancer. And then there were the endless months of pulling myself through surgery and treatments, of trying to fill the absence of Lars, the man I'd rejected. I'd never felt so alone.

The Pacific Ocean raged at me outside my window. I tried not to listen to her saying I was adrift, drowning in voices, a raging sea of negative thoughts. I tried not to listen to the ocean. I tried not to listen to myself. I only wanted Anya to tell me of Ducu's final days, to learn the truth about his death because perhaps this would make sense of my life.

"Sarah?"

"Anya?"

"Am I disturbing you?"

"No, not at all…"

"Because I don't want to disturb you…"

"That's very polite, no you are not disturbing…"

"Because I really want to talk with you. It's been very hard."

"Tell me"

"He's dead. What will I do?"

"It's very hard."

"He suffered so deeply and I tried to help him, but it was too late…they just threw him away, like his life meant nothing. No one understood him and they were so mean…"

"Mean?"

"Yes, and now they just want to throw him away and forget him and I…"

Thrown away. This was his greatest fear. He'd told me that. That all the art in the world wouldn't add up to a life remembered. That he would be forgotten. He had told me about his experience creating a scandal in 1985–at the height of totalitarian rule–that resulted in his identity being taken away for a year because of his production of Popescu's *The Jolly Joker*. Complying with the Communist line, he'd become persona non-grata, isolated by the government and left without a theater where he could create new work. He only spoke of this a few times; he didn't need to say more. It was clear that the experience had scarred him, that he had made a decision never to become invisible again, the trauma nevertheless dragging behind him like a deep shadow.

Let me tell you about Ducu and his Bucharest, a life, a history seen through the lens of my American eyes.

Ducu (Alive)

Rock star of the international theater world, Alexandru "Ducu" Darie was both hero and victim of his own design, a lover and an artist of chaos, and the only man I ever knew who loved his madness as though it were a friend.

A rebel for most of his life, Ducu lived in the shadow of his father, film star Iurie Darie. Born on June 14, 1959, and raised in the public eye of the Teatrul de Comedie of Bucharest, he grew up in the constant attention of Communist Romania. Very tall, Ducu had brown and green eyes that squinted at you through laughter, and his hands were soft against the rough language he preferred. Breaking from convention in the 1980s, he lived a private life in defiance of the state. After 1990, Ducu had many ear piercings, his long hair and striking clothing marking him a punk bon vivant of the 19th century. While discrete about his life, he would still speak publicly of drinking, something that would ultimately lead him to his death at sixty. He was known for his ability to direct comedies, yet his death is seen as tragedy. Once vibrant, annoying, sexy, mournful, generous, and very difficult, his memory a blessing, Ducu remains a pain in the ass.

Self-made, Ducu was an international star for more than thirty years: a director, producer, lighting designer, actor, writer, and opera fiend. Although he was a counter-culture figure in Romania, he nevertheless launched a career in 2006 as the president of the European Theater Union (founded by the great director Giorgio Strehler). Knighted in Romania, Italy, and France for his creative and societal contributions, Ducu also crossed borders with shows in the United States, Israel, Japan, Colombia, Italy, and Russia. At the end of his life, he was Managing Director of Bucharest's famed Bulandra Theater. Burning bright and hard, he was controversial to the end. I believe he was his country: grappling with freedom, creative, untrusting, and often wild.

In December of 1989, Romania had revolted against the tyranny of the Communist party as led by the dictator, Nicolae Ceaușescu. While other segments of Eastern Europe were removing themselves from Communist rule in 1989, Romania and its leadership, were in denial, aiming to maintain their unique police state. Starting on December 21, 1989, Ceaușescu was booed by the people forced into a square to hear one of his monotonous speeches after weeks of bloody violence within the country. At the sound of the jeers, the army shot into the crowd, igniting three days of a revolution that led the army to revolt against the Communist Party, that led to the overtaking of the Palace of the People and the death of Ceaușescu and his much despised wife, Elena. As reported by *The Observer* and chronicled in the book *Tearing Down the Curtain: The People's Revolution in Eastern Europe*, the revolution was swift and deadly:

> Its drama was the stuff of history: the central area in Bucharest, the Palace Square containing both the old palace and the new palace, the Party headquarters, in flames; people crowding round tanks urging the soldiers on; old ladies bringing freshly baked bread to the Army, whose tanks were covered with cheering people. Phrases were shouted aloud that in other circumstances would have sounded mawkish but here thrilled the soul– "You may kill us, but we won't go away."

With the revolution came a high cost of living, years of political conflict, and a future that continues to be confusing.

Born into a family of artists who had some freedom of movement inside Communist Romania, Ducu still grew up in a culture of cruelty. Romanian citizens had to face long food lines because Ceaușescu was exporting their resources. There was little to no heat in winter and the scorch of paranoia bred by the government spread like a disease. Again from the book *Tearing Down The Curtain* on the realities of daily life in Ceaușescu's Romania:

> By law, all typewriters had to be registered with the authorities, together with a copy of their typeface, making the circulation of clandestine pamphlets impossible. There were no photocopiers or duplicating machines. There had been no

> gatherings, meetings or discussion groups as there were in other Eastern countries....The feared secret police, the Securitate, tapped telephones at will and harassed people almost at random and with awesome bureaucratic efficiency. People vanished without a trace...Nobody knew how many political prisoners were in the jail, or even what constituted a political crime.

Ducu emerged from the revolution having taken to the streets with his friends and family in remarkably hopeful spirits, yet the past always haunted him. And though political organization was profoundly difficult in Romania, Ducu and many of his peers had found a way to fight against tyranny through irony and metaphor. They were sophisticated in their communications and this may have given him an edge when entering the post-1989 world.

Bucharest, Ducu's home for his entire life, is an enormous sprawling city of two million people. The center of the city is an homage to the Paris of the 19th century, with a revitalized area once coopted by the Communists, who turned the neighborhood into the controlled dominion of Ceaușescu and his family. They moved into the presidential home (Palatul Primaverii) after he became president in 1965. His wife, Elena, filled the mansion with replicas of western and eastern masterpieces; there are French sitting rooms, huge closets with hundreds of pieces of clothing, a private spa, and a massive indoor pool with murals for the family to enjoy while the citizens died of hunger, illness, and cold. Six peacocks remain in the gardens of the palace while inelegant sculptures adorn the external halls of the grand home. Inside, the smell of fresh linen on the beds is only a small reminder of the laundering of money and the lives of the corrupt leaders. One can sense the deception in this home of tyranny, one can feel the control, the false elegance, the cruel joke of authorities living in splendor while the people suffered.

Circling out and out from the city, the modern buildings meant to house the masses are blunt in design and now hover, often covered in graffiti. People live in apartments and some houses, and continue to share their food and expenses in a complex web of bartering and sharing stemming from the Communist regime, yet allowing for the people to survive together in an economy that's never quite recovered. A member of NATO, Romania is a full EU member but does not yet enjoy complete freedom of travel within other EU countries–a dream of inclusion that's still blocked by their own government's deep investment in corruption.

A ghost of the past Soviet rule remains in Bucharest. Decades of near-slavery, doubts, secrets, and lies have permeated the skin of its people and are visible in the dark circles under the eyes of elders and in the smooth, glossy skin of the young. Patience is a given with Romanians; life is a long line, a struggle as well as desire, a hidden pleasure. The stain of Ceaușescu remains in the air, a dance partner in a historically unfair waltz. Yet, my god, what a gorgeous group of people are found in Bucharest. Elegant and ancient, charming and illusive, the Romanians I've met are beautiful in a complex way, their faces a reflection of Romania's history, from the eastern invasions to the international exploration of Queen Marie. People in Bucharest may look Turkish, Russian, Italian–their faces reflecting invasion or influence from the monarchs who only a century ago claimed Romania as their own. King Carol the First (1839-1914) was selected to be king to oversee the country with ties to Victorian England, the interconnections of that royal family found throughout Europe.

Romanian actors are some of the best in the world. Their training is a combination of the Stanislavsky technique, and of the hard seasons of life, and they have an innate sense of the body and its movement on stage. These actors are thrilling, smart, and determined, able to manage their careers on their own (there are few agents in Romania). In the past ten years, salaries for actors have increased; and so for those artists in permanent positions there is more stability–not so for the independent actors who must create their season and book enough productions to pay the bills. Yet all the actors are like wild horses, moving from theater to theater with their own ideas for productions, and though they live under the thumb of one theater manager or another, they still run wild, creating joy and havoc.

The directors come from a long history of great personalities, and the culture of the Maestro still exists–great directors are still valued here, they win big awards, they fight hard for their turf, they aim to make opuses in the theaters throughout Romania, and most often in Bucharest. Ducu was deeply proud of being a director, and he, along with his peers, felt a connection to the great legacy of the director Liviu Ciulei, born in Communism who later returned to Romania to create works in theaters of the country. Ducu was a trailblazer after the fall of Communism, he traveled abroad, revamping his career and then finding a place for himself in his own country, all of which lead to his being named Director of the famed Bulandra Theater globally perceived as a leader of daring theater styles, directing, and political voice.

Building continues in the city, though there is the constant awareness that earthquakes could take down much of the city. On plaques outside many of the buildings, there's a symbol for those predicted to collapse in the case of earthquake. The acceptance of your fate is a constant in Bucharest. I was told that you may get crushed taking a walk down the street, so enjoy your day! Theaters are often located in storefronts where space has been carved out. These are independent theaters that still have full houses and loyal audience members.

Ducu loved his city. He understood its pace and its need for cultural excitement. Under communism, he had hits at Teatrul de Comedie in the old center, a meeting place for the rulers who permitted citizens to experience theater as their guests. Ducu's production of *Amadeus* is still remembered as a treasure celebrating the freedom of Mozart. It dangerously took on the corruption of Holy Roman Emperor Joseph II as a metaphor for Ceaușescu's political class. Mozart was one of Ducu's heroes, and they had many similarities: both loved music, romance, and revels, both were high-level Masons who struggled at the end of their lives with illness, and both battled against the status quo, defending their need to be wild. Neither Ducu nor Mozart died rich; each has a simple grave. Both were called slightly silly but they but they seemed to be touched by the creative finger of God.

Yet even though he had to cope with the state's failures, he was hilarious: the funniest person I knew.

Teatrul de Comedie (The Comedy Theater) sits at 2 Dumitru Street in Bucharest, standing in defiance of the mundane. It's a place people enter to laugh, to turn their thoughts away from pain, to get a lift, a high from life.

The theater was founded in 1960 by Radu Beligan with the intent to provide the public with wonderful, accessible comedy. As the theater advanced, its audience also grew. The police state that was Romania was wary of artists and therefore kept a close eye on the rising theater. The theater states about its history: "Under the general mask of comedy and satire…(the theater was able to pass)… more easily over the obstacles placed by the authorities of the time." Teatrul de Comedie became a place where you could play with the fire of irony, politics, and freedom of expression. It was not just fun and games at this theater, it was a place for radical laughter.

It is explained to me that Teatrul de Comedie was one of many theaters that supported radical art in times of tyranny. The Bulandra, Teatrul Mic, Teatrul de Stat Oradea and the National Theater–these created a web of voices and styles that gave life and energy toward the peoples' search for authentic voice in the world. Under Communist rule, Romanian theater flourished in opaque rebellion, and later, when Ducu took over the Bulandra Theater, many hoped the risk and innovation of the past would continue through him. Yet it was what was funny that drove Ducu, even if what was funny on stage uncovered what was terrible in the world.

Romanian humor is an art form unto itself. Unlike most western theater, Romanian humor calls attention to irony in subtle, unspoken ways: an eye roll, a gesture, unsaid moments between people. Developed as a tool against oppression, the humor of Romania is a code. Within the code lie decades of practice, combined with the elegant tradition of classical theater. Romania (and Teatrul de Comedie) created a layered and exciting art. Along with the Romanian tradition of joke telling (something Ducu made into a fine art throughout his life), Teatrul de Comedie brought spectacle and visual magic into the work.

In *A History of Romanian Theater from Communism to Capitalism: Children of a Restless Time*, critic and theater journalist Cristina Modreanu writes about the "code" or, as she describes it, "underground speaking" that fueled Communist-era Romanian theater:

> This kind of "underground speaking" was common in theatre productions and it had become standard for actors to use classics to parody the political system and its main figures. To do so, they used language–allusions, metaphors, citations from public speeches–placed in old plays to make connections to the real world and the terrors of the regime.

The life at that theater was rich in subtext, and Ducu was to spend his youth at the heart of it. And thank goodness for the relative safety of the theater, for Romania was caught in the vise of history and geography. As Robert D. Kaplan writes in his comprehensive book *In Europe's Shadow: Two Cold Wars and a Thirty-Year Journey through Romania and Beyond*:

> As tragic as Romanian history has been, the Communist epoch raised suffering to an unprecedented level...The end of World War II had given Romania little or no respite. From early 1944, the Western Allies recognized that the war

inside Romania and the peace that followed, therefore, was "Russia's business."

"This bleak state of affairs was primarily the consequence of geography", writes British historian Hugh Thomas in *Armed Truce: The Beginnings of the Cold War 1945-1946.* "A place between two totalitarian empires, the German Nazi one and the Soviet Russian, is unenviable." The humanitarian consequence of such geography during the early phases of the Cold War was simply appalling.

To be frank, there was nothing at all funny about life in Romania after World War II and into the Cold War. To maintain a stranglehold on the citizens of Romania, humor, free speech, and individual thought were strictly regulated. That's why the Teatrul de Comedie was so remarkable: its compass pointed toward creative expression in a time regulated for no thought, no freedom, and no kindness.

In this harsh context of dictatorship, Ducu was born at seven months on the 14th of June, 1959. He was the son of two artists of the Comedy Theater, Consuela Rosu and Iurie Darie. Though he was born prematurely, his devoted parents embraced him completely–his mother breastfed him. And Iurie, returning from the theater, would hold him through the night. Consuela had been raised in a circus and later became an actress, and then a deeply insightful mother. Iurie was a gallant leading man, elegant, funny (as well as a gifted artist), and was as successful on stage as he was in film and television.

As an American, I see Ducu as though he were Steve McQueen's son–surrounded by people watching, standing before cameras set up by the studio (in this case, the State)–his parents were always being watched by audiences and by the government. There are pictures of them together and they look brooding and beautiful; they knew how to pose–they knew how to hide in plain sight. In photographs, his mother and father tend to look sideways at the lens, their mouths are curled into practiced smiles and their cheekbones look fabulous; they are stars. Ducu is generally gazing defiantly into the camera, his eyes huge and his mouth tight. He is not an obvious star, but unrelentingly present, a force of nature that doesn't fear the lens.

On Romanian television's *Backstage* in 1999, Iurie and Ducu did a joint interview with Ducu about his childhood. Ducu spoke of remembering being taken to the theater (because they did not have babysitters), the sound of his father's voice, the smell of Teatrul de Comedie's stage, his parents acting together and his first time on stage in Shakespeare's *Troilus and Cressida*. In that production, he'd played

Myrmidon, an ancient Greek soldier of Achilles. Ducu's memory was very specific, he explained that when he played the small role as a soldier he was set to "kill" his father in a grand fight scene. Yet one day during rehearsal, Ducu sat in the theater and for the first time, realized his father was acting–he must have assumed Iurie was able to die and come back to life. Later, after Ducu returned to the stage, Iurie told of being "stabbed" extremely hard, which broke his concentration. Looking up, he saw Ducu intensely trying to kill him. Ducu wasn't really trying to kill his father, but was instead trying to break the veil of a stage, to find what was real, to draw blood in his imagination.

This memory is poignant for me because Ducu loved his father yet lived his life having to make extra space for himself in the world. He certainly did not want to kill off his father, yet he had to find a way to take the stage himself. He soon decided that being a director would help him have his own voice, his own place on the stage.

Ducu explained in the interview that he decided not to become an actor but a director. Lucky to have the support of his parents, he asked to attend the National University of Theater and Cinematic Art. Desiring to gain acceptance into the school on his own merits, he implored his father not to talk to anyone there. Ducu said in the interview that he was terrified by the idea that people would think his father got him into the school. Nepotism and bribes were integral to the Communist way, and Ducu wanted a clean entry into his creative life. Iurie agreed to stay silent, but he warned Ducu of the double-edged sword, that Ducu might not get into the school even with his father's help.

As fate would have it, Ducu received one of the three spots open at the school, and though he was offered a slot, he was first told to serve in the army before becoming a director. Ducu served his time and learned to shoot a gun, then came back hungry to make theater, later to graduate in 1983.

How did Consuela and Iurie raise such a confident person in such dangerous times?

Perhaps the answer is that they took their son to the theater as soon as he was born and he never left it. He must have been imbued with the feelings and jokes of Teatrul de Comedie, the laughter of audiences becoming as close and consistent as family. He was safe inside comedy; he was free from a world of hate.

Nicolae Ceaușescu rose to power in Romania in the early 1960s. Steely in his resolve to control the country, the dictator starved and bored the people for decades until they took humor underground. Movies were made in Romania according to Communist code, yet international films were smuggled into the country for view. The actors encoded their own personal language to hide the truth, and the theater found ways to convey the life of Romania through layers of humor.

I imagine the Romanian actors and directors glittering, sardonic, and alive, each one held for long curtain calls, lauded by fans as they walked the streets, given flowers in the dead of winter. The theater, a place to be free, yes, but also a place identified by the State as potentially dangerous.

Describing his early life as magical, Ducu rejected school as something deeply boring and stupid. So he gave himself to the life of the theater where he was free to draw, listen, and (his favorite) watch. It was all part of breathing life in a place where ghosts roamed the stage and pretty actresses lavished attention on him. Early on, he learned to see things for himself, to accept the surprise of the stage and to appreciate a good laugh.

It was probably in this theater that Ducu became a believer in ritual and ghosts. He was a superstitious person by nature, and in the theater there were years of traditions meant to ward off evil spirits, to encourage a "full house" of audiences, to gain good health and luck. Later in life, Ducu would adorn his neck with dozens of necklaces with ornaments and icons to help protect him. He believed that energy could help or harm you; the theater had taught him to believe in the unknown, and in those years he would become obsessed with being protected from the dangers of the outside world, and particularly from the politicians and governments he grew to distrust. He would mention "auras" as casually as one mentions coffee. He was a bit of a superstitious fruitcake at times, and could be hurtful with quick judgments if he felt there was an "evil eye" on a person or project.

For Ducu, ghosts were everywhere. Phantoms lived in the empty seats of any theater. Memories could carry on as feelings, tangible to the eye when the lights were dimming. Costumes had authentic energy and could exude the essence of a character. People had souls and those souls could live in the walls of a theater, forever. Emerging from Romania after the revolution in 1989, Ducu would assess the artistic weight of a theater through his sense of ghosts.

In New York, he told me he found few ghosts because America was too young, too arrogant. In London, he felt the presence of Oscar Wilde and Shakespeare and would whisper to them from the plush velvet seats. In Paris, he felt Molière, wild and free, floating low across the stage of the grand Odeon Theater. In Romania, he felt the ghosts of his past, the past of his country, as though it had a body that it had to drag across the stage in each play. Yes, ghosts were everywhere.

But Ducu could be a real asshole. He avoided important telephone calls. He hated to make choices in life. He laughed at others when they adored him. He was that "popular" kid in high school whom you knew was dangerous but you wanted to sleep with anyway. His eyes could be cruel. He could make selfish decisions. He could taunt authority. He did all this, and then he smiled, and it would melt the room–he was a master of charm and many people would ultimately find that they would do anything for him.

In the beginning, he was a child of the theater who did not know there was life beyond a curtain: he came to believe that what was unreal was real, and he was shaped to live in a time all its own. Because there was only the time of the stage, Ducu grew up singularly unaware of clocks. Consistently late his entire life, he never rushed anywhere but lived to the timing of a good joke: if you wait for it, let it land, the laugh will feel like forever. He was never aware that time could be different for other people, and quite frankly, his rude tardiness drove everyone crazy.

Ducu gave an interview in 2011, ironically for a Silva beer special, in which he spoke of time and his relationship to it: "When an actor is onstage and forgets his lines, it is a few seconds, but for the actor who goes 'blank' it feels like hours", Ducu said. "When you are in rehearsal, you practice the same lines for days and days, but when you are on stage, those lines go by so fast. The same is with life, moments go by very, very fast, especially when they are the happiest moments."

And in every fleeting moment, there was Consuela. Centered, intelligent, his mother kept the apartment filled with books and guided her son as best she could to a meaningful life of the mind. Ducu spoke of his mother's life, and early death, with deep love: he felt seen by her, and he saw her intellect and creativity as a gift he lost too soon.

Devoted mother and working actress, Consuela was at the theater as much, or more, than at their home, and she probably managed a good deal of Ducu's care on her own. To say that Ducu was a highly energetic child is an understatement; he was always making or moving, playing games or breaking rules. Yet Ducu and his mother had a deep connection–he valued her opinion, even wanted her approval. As an artist, Consuela was extremely elegant, engaging, and open minded; she shaped their life to the flow between the theater and the day-to-day world outside of the arts.

Consuela died early of cancer in 1986 (only a year after Ducu became persona non grata for his production of *Jolly Joker*). Her death was a shock to him, and her absence never left him. Although he had a career working with men to create all forms of art, women played a key role in his work throughout his life. And if the solidity of his parents' marriage was a guide for his life, Ducu sought longstanding creative partnerships to make productions.

For thirty or more years, Ducu collaborated with Maria Miu on productions that dazzled, made trouble, and most importantly, moved audiences. Ducu trusted Maria's eye and taste above those of most people. If there was a fight to be had about the vision of a show, he listened to her and was guided by her eye. In this way, they became one body–a body born in the context of totalitarianism, and their rebellion against it was to create art that made you feel free. Their partnership was love, yes, and it was also defiance against a loss of vision and the seemingly constant threat to art. I picture them never stopping for time in the 1990s, and even in the 2000s when they divorced but nevertheless together continued to push their body of work into a new era for Romania.

In the theater, it's not unusual for couples to blend their creative and personal lives. Perhaps this is because the world of the theater has its own pacing, sense of time, and rules. And certainly, for most artists, being different is lonely. Couples can protect each other from the harshness of life and the risk of expressing your inner world. Ducu and Maria had this remarkable life of art, and history should hold them up as one of the great creative teams of Europe.

The theater is a very patriarchal place. Men are meant to be directors and women to "support" them. In this way, Ducu was not changing any trends by working with women in Romania (although he empowered many to take decision-making roles). Cristina Modreanu speaks to the patriarchy of Romanian theater post 1989, in *The History of Romanian Theatre from Communism to Capitalism*:

> The patriarchal model is unfortunately very popular in the artists area too, where 95 percent of the decision-makers are men, even though, for example, both staff and artistic teams in the theatre are composed mostly of women.

That said, Ducu had a lot of doubts about men in power. He didn't appear to believe that just because you were a guy you had the right stuff to make magic and lead people into art. Perhaps because of this, he worked with and promoted women as directors, designers, writers, and managers. He trusted women in powerful roles with a great deal of intention. When he became the General Manager of the Bulandra Theater in 2002, he brought his deeply personal (if boundary-less) management and creative style to bear, and he brought those he was close to into the fold of his administration. Every family has a "system" and Ducu had his system. His need for emotion and risk created a certain kind of culture that demanded loyalty to his vision, while also establishing a tight-knit team to create safety.

Ducu believed that a creative team was a family. So though he partnered with men to make art, the women often led the way in the creative endeavor to protect "the family." Though he appeared to admire fierceness, Ducu wanted a protective vibe around rehearsals and creative planning. He demanded an intimacy that crossed boundaries: people drinking, crying, feeling, and laughing together into late hours. He wanted the life inside a theater to feel like a vibrant home, and he pushed back on anyone who wanted him to be professionally "normal." Therefore, his "home" in a theater was filled with intimacy, the collective happiness of everyone shifting according to the degree of their closeness to each other — and sometimes this created a mess.

It is difficult not to fall into clichés while exploring Ducu's partnerships with women, especially if you accept that gender is a construct. Yet it is possible that Ducu thought that women were more connected to feelings, though he knew that women are as tough as men. Because he valued feelings as much as he did thought, Ducu believed that feelings are the lifeblood of the theater. He also allowed himself to live a more deeply emotional life, and often looked to women on his team to help him manage his feelings–feelings that were often large, sensitive and in need of care. These feelings were especially intense because he had no room for machismo when it came to exploring the emotions of a play; he could leave the conventional construct of a man at the door, and in rehearsal, he met everyone on an emotional level that transformed the idea of artmaking. For Ducu, empathy was empathy, and so he could walk in the shoes of a woman as well as in the shoes of a man. This made him unbelievably attractive to people; he could understand you very quickly, and make you feel you were in a simultaneous act of seduction and communion. Did he learn this ability from women? Did it matter to him? I still don't know. What mattered to him was being free to be who you are, while also feeling you were part of a family.

But all this talk of family did not stop him from being sexy. Sensuality and sex played a large role in Ducu's work. He loved to see people try to connect on stage, and he was unabashed to show sexuality. A sexy person, he liked sexy content. Throughout his work, you can see his interest in couples, how they connect or not.

He once directed a play by the Marquis de Sade in Bogota. Away from his Romanian audience, he explored sexuality more deeply, diving into the ways in which people love, how they connected, how they did not. He wanted to explore what sex meant to you as a viewer, what turned you on. He was also curious about how sexuality was expressed and experienced differently for men and women. He seemed to have done more of this exploration of sex and gender when working internationally, perhaps because of the social mores of Romania, but perhaps because he didn't know the audience and had more freedom in his mind to explore.

The American writer Gertrude Stein said, "I write for myself and strangers." Ducu did this, he freely presented his vision to strangers, refusing, however, to shape his work to pander to any particular audience. As he grew older, perhaps wiser, he began to look at the less sexual elements of connection, beyond the sexual, and he worked on stage with texts showing families in conflict rather than romantic stories of couples. He matured in this way, yet his reputation for fearlessness remained in the countries where he made work.

Ducu once sat nude for a compilation of Romanian portraits showing the body. His body was his place of worship.

"I believe in theater that is made with blood", Ducu in the last year his life said. "Theater keeps me alive. I have always made theater made of love, not of fear. Theater is the only art invented by mankind that shows what you don't see." Art being born of blood–yes, vital for Ducu, as all of the artists close to him confirmed to me, the idea one of Ducu's most important discoveries for himself. He loved the theater as much as he loved life. He surrendered himself completely to the theater he made with others, even throughout the illness that ultimately killed him. This often put him at odds with Romania, a place that can be both unconventionally wild and wildly conventional. Though he was a star abroad, he was also called "strange" in Romania. Yet, again, he projected the opinion that he did not care–he had been to and worked in a dozen countries to make theater and live his life, and in those places he'd found an inner freedom with no need to label himself. Instead, he focused on the ephemeral excitement of creative and personal partnerships and brought this learning back to Bucharest.

To the end, Ducu stayed loyal to himself first and then to his team of artists, a combination of strong women and open-minded men. This, in my opinion, makes his legacy genderless and his love of the family of theater one of his defining traits. For the big idea that Ducu embodied is that men and women could work together, as family. This may seem obvious, but it's not obvious in a theater environment that still reflects the rest of the world: women very often get left out of the deep creative process, unlike men who are simply let into the club. An auteur director who demanded the vision be his and his alone, he nevertheless did share, with both women and men.

The truth, though, is that time haunted Ducu. He had to balance the time he was able to manage in the theater with his sense of lost time under Communism. He could be in the moment, and then in the next moment weep because he was thrown into a memory. The trauma that Ducu (and all Romanians under Ceaușescu's rule) experienced was real. The negation of the self, the threats of death, unknown violations, the starvation and shame, all have had a lasting imprint on the people of Romania to this day. Yet for Ducu, in the year he had his identity taken for acting against the state (*Jolly Joker*, 1984-1985), he paid a price; he never forgot it and at times he seemed to feel it had just happened. One might argue that this was his first experience in exile.

Having his soul and person erased for a year, I believe, started a trend for Ducu; that of inner exile, where he never felt totally at home again and was most comfortable in other countries, yet was constantly drawn back to Romania with the hope that she would be kinder. From my perspective, he never seemed to feel he had a truly safe place to land. And so, drinking, perhaps, became his way of coping with the pressure of his own fame, responsibilities, and internal experience of feeling on the outside, something he'd long felt because of his father's fame and entitlements.

Unfortunately, the population of Romania is the fifteenth highest consumer of alcohol in the world at 13.7 liters of pure alcohol per capita (World Health Organization, 2016), with little to no cultural (or psychological) support for those suffering with addiction. Additionally, post-Soviet Union, Moscow's decades long campaigns to dissuade drinking were canceled and Eastern Europe as a whole saw a fifty percent increase in alcohol consumption (per IZA,

World of Labor, Evgeny Yakovlev). The region was filled with alcohol, leaving Ducu (and others) under its toxic spell.

Even with the hard living, Ducu had a career where almost every one of his plays was a hit, and he was consistently growing and at the top of his skills as an artist. His trauma may have been very real, yet he seemed to find a place of happiness that brought him out enough to work on a new play. He used Teatrul de Comedie as his creative DNA. "Luckily" for his audience, comedy thrives in those who feel they are on the outside of culture, and so amidst the applause, his inner exile thrived, while his inner demons used the theater to survive.

How do you do funny when you are in hell? I didn't know the answer to that question until I first went to Bucharest and spent most of my time laughing my ass off. Although the city is a bit worn down, the life of Bucharest is vibrant and awake. As in New York, the people don't sleep, and they spend a good amount of their time in cafés telling stories surrounded by smoke and stiff drinks. Because the city is alive and the people demanding of fun, humor is the electricity for their glittering nights.

Though I first saw Bucharest only in 2018, I can imagine how the elegant spark of Teatrul de

Comedie lit up groups of friends at the height of tyranny. Hiding their joy, they would gather at the theater to catch a smile, to sit in soft seats, and enjoy the rolling of actors' eyes and the pink lips of leading ladies.

When I picture Ducu in his own world as a young teen, I imagine him already sitting with his legs crossed at the knee. By his early teens, he would have seen a good amount of Molière and known the proper way to lean into farce. He probably started smoking then, too, bumming cigarettes off the stage-hands. Perhaps he stood alone on stage in the after-noons and counted the lights that hung above him.

But it is all about timing, says every comic in the world. Timing is the life-blood of a joke, and Ducu spent eighteen years as a kid at Teatrul de Comedie studying the craft. So irony was something he learned early, and this probably set him apart from the other kids who were being trained to see "progress for the State" as the meaning of life. For Ducu, comedy was proof that nothing is set in stone, that "funny" is the belief that nothing makes total sense, that our desire to control our outcomes is pointless, and hilarious.

When you direct comedy, you must always be aware of the truth of pain buried in the story. When Ducu directed anything funny, he was able to amplify the moments of deep despair with very funny, desperate action: his characters ran, fell, grabbed, stumbled, shook, begged, danced, seduced, lied–all the things he saw when he was growing up in a culture dictated by a lie; the lie of freedom found only in authoritarian rule. He never forgot the anguish of being hidden away from the world, and his characters were free to be manic failures in a drama they had no control over.

The truth is that Ducu specialized in humor because he knew what hate looked like. And the hate he was born into became the canvas for his art and a private life that could appear like farce. Ducu was neither a "Romeo" nor a "Casanova"–he was more than that, he was a deep adventurer, and he protected this identity from a Romanian culture steeped in judgment and cruel opinions. So if you were his friend, you were part of a story that had to have a sense of humor, passion, and a brave commitment to a long connection with him. Many think the way to remember him is through pictures of him telling actors what to do on a stage. Yet I would argue that it's quite the opposite–to remember him in his brave defiance of the status quo and bourgeois conventions is what I would suggest. Defiance is what makes him such an interesting person, and it was his love of searching that made him such a thrilling artist.

What is also true is that the man loved a great suit. It did not matter if it was cut for him, or cut to fit a woman, if it was well-made he would wear it. Ducu's love of style brought him into the world of fashion where he directed runway shows, music videos, and concerts in Romania. He loved the change inherent in fashion, and he took grief from people (and from gossip) that this made him effete. Laughing, he once told me he did "*not* give a fuck" about the people in Romania who thought his earrings made him gay.

Style was his weapon. He wore his hair chopped, long in a ponytail, curly and big, or cropped to the head like a Roman sentry. He put loops in his left ear, studs climbed up his right ear that seemed to catch light and draw attention to his eyes. He wore colors that clashed, ties that did not match his socks, scarves that did not match his jackets, all this mixing and matching were usually en vogue with the color blocks found in magazines, yet not worn by the people in power around him. He didn't exercise and was proud of his belly. His long legs looked great in jeans and he wore his shirt out, messy and cool like a kid. For a person so very tall, his feet were a bit small, but this did not stop him from wearing hip shoes for men. He always had a cigarette lit. He was caught once with a "man purse." He wore long Indian shirts and folded himself in floor-length coats that from behind made him look like a sea captain. His necklaces and the rings on his fingers had symbolism. He was a walking fashion statement that seemed to say, "Fuck you, very much."

No one owned Ducu. And he had no time for our small mindedness, our conflicts over our freedom, our cruel judgments borne of human foibles. Yet he was a director, and so he had pity for us, saw us in all of our stuck and frightened lives and took our silliness to the stage, where he built worlds where we could recognize society without having the awareness that it was we whom he was capturing in time. We were all of the characters in his comedy.

We were the madness.

We were dangerous and we needed to be laughed at, constantly.

(We were, to the very end, players in his play.)

Alexandru "Ducu" Darie (Dead)

"You see, in the end he was an artist and they did not understand", Anya said, forcefully, to me. "They did not understand his last work. They did not appreciate his legacy. They just left him to die. They did not understand his blood"

(There it is again: "I believe in theater that is made with blood... Theater keeps me alive. I have always made theater made of love, not of fear." But the truth of the matter is that this "theater made of blood" included Ducu's own. He had suffered quietly, growing thinner and smaller. He tried every cure and changed his eating. Nothing worked. Finally, used to a lifetime of gossip, he put his head down and did the work; he used the theater as oxygen to keep himself alive.)

"His blood was the theater, you know?" Anya insisted. We were speaking again on the phone.

"Yes, yes, I know."

"I am an actress and that's how we met."

"Anya, I'm interested in his final days."

She paused, the feeling was heavy. "Did you try to help him, Sarah?"

I felt as though shame was punching me in the stomach. "I sent him medicine", I said, finally, "and tried to convince him to come to California for treatment."

She gasped. "Oh, he did not tell me. Oh!"

"But what's wrong?" I said.

I could hear her far away breath, feel her very deep feelings, sense a "rapidness" to her body. I listened to the rise and fall of her inside my phone.

"In the end, everyone rejected him", Anya said.

"Why?"

"Because of his genius. And, the drinking. They all called him a drunk. Now, they want to forget him. Can you come to Bucharest?"

I looked out the window at nothing. There was only air outside, and inside me there was nothing as well.

"Bucharest?"

"Yes, please. You can come here and I can offer you the apartment. It's the least I can do…he loved you so much."

He had, hadn't he? Yes, I know he had. Though he had not told me about Anya, we had always talked about our relationships, but that did not mean he didn't love me, right?

"Please come to Bucharest", she pleaded. "Have you been here? You should come here before it's all gone."

(Before it's all gone.)

As she spoke, I fully remembered his lips on my neck. He had kissed my body for the last time in 2018 when, much like this time, an actress had pleaded I come to see him before he died. I had then called all of the doctors I knew, each one sad and each one sorry that there was no known cure for liver disease, "I'm so sorry, Sarah. Really. But, you should go to say goodbye", they had said. I heard each one tell me the truth, yet remarkably, I was able to push that reality aside with a wish for miracles. I researched every holistic cure and created a box filled with remedies and books, lucky objects, and vitamins that I mailed to the theater for Ducu. I also contacted people in the United States who were connected to cancer care centers in case I found he had cancer and needed a second opinion. Searching online, I discovered the alternative reality of the Internet, and I nearly went mad.

When illness comes upon you, you might become deeply immersed in the work of researching a different ending. The Internet is like a drug of promise, and in it I'd found answers in turmeric, cannabis, anti-inflammatory cures, you name it. Ducu was already using homeopathic cures and felt they had a positive impact on his mood and body, though deep down he must have known they were not going to change the course his body was taking–deep down, I knew it, too, yet kept my head in the sand.

A week later in the spring of 2018, I had boarded a flight to a place I did not know. As the plane flew the many hours over the sea and then over land, I looked down at the railway tracks of Europe. I could imagine how they had transported my relations, the Jews, across the vast flats of Germany and Poland, the smoke from the trains merging with the smoke from the concentration camps ahead. And then the beauty of the Carpathian Mountains hit me with their vibrant green and deep brown. Here, the boundaries told the stories of trainloads of Russians overtaking the small nation of Romania–their King forced to board a train into the obscure hell of being a noble refugee. The rivers told the story of invasion, and of vodka poured into the people to numb them and Ducu into submission for over sixty years. I landed in Bucharest in tears, the story of Ducu's life, the ravages of war and dictatorship finally real.

It was May, and the city was soft with light. My apartment was across the street from the National Theater and on the boulevard where much of the revolution of 1989 had taken place. I walked the streets in the morning, taking in the sculptures, the aging deco buildings, the lovely large streets with cafés open for business. I waited several days for a response from Ducu, and during that time became acquainted with his city, a place I'd held in my inner dialogue for decades. I saw a production of *Hamlet*, met with artists I had connected with through Facebook, and discovered a world unlike my own.

Bucharest was far more romantic than I had imagined: the people I met had a desire to find meaning in creativity and art, and the community of friendship was lovely. I could see how deeply difficult it must have been for Ducu to think of leaving, and I also thought of the millions of people who had chosen to leave Romania to find work and healthcare for their families.

Though I was fascinated by his country, Ducu did not seem fascinated with me. I was in Bucharest for three days and he did not respond to my text messages or emails. I had flown across the world for him and he, as usual, was on his own time and did not answer. I woke early and walked the streets in the morning, people passing crisply on their hunt for coffee.

I looked for him as I had looked for him in other countries: walking in the streets. You see, Ducu had a gait that was unmistakable–he was a heavy walker and one of his feet turned inward, he always walked fast and seemed to talk to himself. If he had a long jacket, it would billow behind him; if it was warm, he wore tee-shirts that appeared to be pulled at the neck.

So I looked for him in Bucharest. I imagined him walking quickly to and from the theater. I imagined him ten feet in front of me. I was sure I saw him turn a corner and go out of sight. I was sure he was exiting a car. I was sure I was waiting, as we all must, for him to appear.

This did not stop me from acting like an idiot. I walked through the streets trying to catch his scent in the air. I was pulled back into the young woman I had been when we met, when I could imagine love as fresh, when I could justify loving him as an act of rebellion. I wandered the streets trying to pick up his smell, and all I could gather were the remnants of his cologne, it pressed through me as I looked at the architecture and the city planning, like that of Paris, though this city was falling apart. Yet, this time in my life, I did not fall apart waiting for him, I stood my ground–I waited for his call, patient, like a 19th century parlor game, the handwritten letters now emails, the friends helping us to connect like characters in a novel.

So, I waited.

After several days in Bucharest and much coordination later, Ducu and I met. I understood later that he had paced his theater hall before seeing me. I also paced in the garden of the café. I was told he was waiting for me in a small bookstore, and so I allowed myself to wander up a flight of stairs, I could smell his perfume. And then I saw him. He was sitting on a small chair. He pulled his hand through his blunt hair, all the earrings we had pierced into his left ear were now gone, his fingers shook. He looked like he had AIDS.

I saw him in his deep frailty because his realness made me reel, it gave me the gift: I had to see him as he was, and that I–if I dispensed caution in my rough American way–could break him.

Our hug was delicate and strange. I held his elbows in my palms as he laid his head on my right shoulder like a little boy. The moment was not long enough.

Ducu and I walked down a long staircase without saying a word to each other. We entered a room to talk. We sat in two chairs and he took my hand and told me of his sickness–yes, he had liver disease, but no, the reports of cancer were wrong. I wept. He watched me. I asked him if he needed anything, and no, no, he was simply happy I was there. I asked if he minded that I had dedicated a novel to him, and if it was okay if I wrote about our relationship. He paused, looked me in the eye, and said he wanted me to tell the truth, "With everything, tell the truth." Then, with eyebrow lifted he said, "It's like you have always been in Bucharest." I winked at him and then he asked me to dinner for the next evening.

The next day, I met him at the theater. He was not in the hall when I arrived, so I sat alone in the sandy planes of his production of *Coriolanus*. A few actors were sitting on chairs and I smelled the room. I could feel the words of *Coriolanus*. The ripped up walls reminded me of his life, carefully exposed, carefully hidden but so very raw.

I was not feeling a bit romantic. I was tired, I was older and all I could think of was how we were back in a theater, but how I had no energy for bed. Smiling, he slowly came down the steps, introduced me to his actors and we left through the catacombs of the theater.

We crossed the street into the park that sits across from the theater. Instead of going straight to the restaurant, he wanted to sit on a bench. Gasping for air, he turned to me and said, "I'm so tired. So tired of being 'nudgy.' So tired of being mad." I put my hand on the back of his neck and nodded. I took those full seconds in with desire, a lust for intimacy and truth. He leaned back into my hand, I felt his spine on my wrist. In those seconds, his spine told me everything: how his body was failing, how time was not on his side, how time was an abstraction for our relationship. His body told me of a search he had been on for decades–a search for his place in the world–a search for his meaning–a search for his ghosts. I felt his experience of the world through his skin, as though it could sing with little breath left. Yes, he'd traveled the world, yes, he'd made art everywhere, but now, his time was coming to an end. It was unbearable, receiving all this through his still soft skin. So much truth I found myself trying to smile, as though that would ease the pain of endings.

"Come on, let's go eat", he said. "Yes", I responded, both too tired to get up. Sitting forward, we said, "One, two, three", and then rose. My ankle gave way and I stumbled as we walked on the gravel. He grabbed my arm, and we swayed. "Fuck", we both said, and then I spoke, "When did we get so *old*?" He laughed as hard as he could through coughing, then shook his head, his hand at my back as we entered the restaurant. Over soup and meats, salads and dessert, we covered as much as we could, called friends in the United States and Italy whom he spoke with in whatever language they wished and we took a picture together as he sweetly placed his hand on my ass. We laughed.

I told him my best boob jokes, the ones you learn when you have breast cancer. He told me a new joke of his that I swiftly forgot in lieu of a memory of his smile. We did not count minutes. We did not have a sense of time. We talked until it was dark, then he drove me to another theater.

I touched his hair, he kissed my neck–soft, long movements that felt like the past. He then told me he loved me. I told him the same. I never felt his body again.

I watched his car pull away from me. The course of my life had shifted in that goodbye. I had no idea if I should turn left or right. I had no idea if I should run after him. The light was long and the evening was warm. I remembered his face, young, laughing. I thought of his mouth on mine so long ago, and wondered why he hid his lips from me now.

His departure caused the deep territorial lines in me to buckle, to cave in, and I was left with our experience no longer like a hole in the Berlin Wall, no, this time it was a hole in my sense of time. In that moment, I thought he was one of the few people I really knew in the world. Though I had a million questions, once he drove away I did not write them down, they just lifted into the night air as I stood before the Jewish Theater, the smell of tea coming from a café.

(Before it's all gone...That's where Anya had left it with me. Yes, I knew what it meant to have it all go away.)

Now, in 2019, a few days after his death, Anya spoke to me on the phone: "Please, Sarah, come to Bucharest. They will be showing his *Coriolanus* for the last time. After that, they are throwing the production away."

"Throwing it away? How is that possible?"

"I told you. They don't want him remembered, my Ducu, they want his memory gone, like he was nothing."

"I grew up in the theater."

"Yes, I know. Ducu told me."

"Aha, well, this happens in the theater. People like to control the memory of a theater–it happens."

"But it should not happen to him! Please visit."

"I suppose I could write about him?"

"Yes! I will help you. I know publishers and people who can help us. Please!"

I hung up the phone feeling needed. I had not felt that in a long time. I felt deep down that I'd been rejected by Ducu in the end. He'd loved me but he'd never let me in at the end of his life–never let me help, the only thing I'd wanted to give–help. And in that moment, I had a picture of the life I felt should not be forgotten, about his country, about his comedy in the face of hate, of the women he worked with–arm in arm, hand in hand, he'd always worked well with women.

I lay on my bed and thought about leaving. If I could pull the money together, I could leave in a few weeks, before December began, then see his final production–find an ending.

The next day, Anya called me. "I'm sorry if I was too crazy, too emotional yesterday."

"No, I just…it must be very emotional for you."

"It was emotional talking to you because he loved you so much, and then I could speak with you."

I heard laughter in the background. A high, cackling sound. A woman and perhaps a man were in the distance.

"What is that?" I asked.

"Oh, my friends. They knew Ducu well, and we are just here, trying to laugh. It's so awful here. Wait…"

Anya pulled the phone away, perhaps she put her hand over the speaker. She returned.

"My friend Peter is laughing at my terrible English. He is disgusted by how bad it is…wait, he wants to talk to you."

I heard the phone move between hands.

"Hello? Sarah?"

"Yes?"

"This is Peter. She is crazy–Anya. She thinks she can speak English…" He laughed.

"I think she sounds fine"

"No, it's awful. Ducu spoke perfect English…"

"You knew Ducu?"

"He was like my brother, my father, my…" Peter grew quiet, it sounded as though he was crying.

"You loved him?" I asked, the question familiar to me because I had been asking this question, to myself, for decades.

Peter seemed to walk away from the sounds of voices. He pulled the phone close to his mouth. "Please, come visit, these women are driving me crazy. They don't understand what we have lost with Ducu dying…the theater is over, the world is…"

"Less." I said.

"Yes! Less. He took it all with him, he took it all."

"Peter, may I call you later to understand better what is going on?"

"Of course! It would be my pleasure. I loved him."

"I can hear that."

"And I want to tell you. I want to remember him with you."

"I'd like that."

The phone dropped. I tried to call back but no one answered. I looked at my watch. It was time to go to yoga and cry. Pulling myself from the bed, I peeled my clothes off and stood naked in front of the mirror. Ducu had only been dead a few days and my body was a stranger to me.

When I'd seen him last, we had been older, frailer, not soft and beautiful as we were when we were kids. Turning sideways, I looked at myself from the back–who was I now?

Now, with his body gone from the world, how would I fit into my own body? I had no answer, but slipped on the second skin of yoga attire and made my way to the garage, my flip - flops smacking the floor as I escaped my apartment.

I drove my car the eight blocks to yoga and signed in, silent, grabbing a small towel for the sweat and tears. I entered the studio; it was silent, I was silent. I lay on a mat and imagined what Ducu would do if he could watch a yoga class–who would he look at, would he meditate, whose ass would he like to watch? I imagined him sitting on the floor, smoking, coyly smiling at the downward dog movements and the child's pose; he'd enjoy that.

The class began, and as though on cue, the tears came up as I moved up and down, my stomach aching and my tendons worn from walking in boots for too many years. "Baby…" I imagined him saying to me while sitting on the floor, watching. "You should have told me about yoga earlier! Look at this, it's fantastic!"

When class was over, I drove home. I did not see anyone I knew. There was little traffic. It was innocuous, it was plain–it was not the state of my birth, New York. I live in a small town-like city on the edge of the Pacific Ocean that might have harbored bandits one hundred years ago, though now it's just regular people, clinging to the side of the United States, hoping not to fall in. I've spent decades thinking I should have lived in Europe, and those thoughts colored the way I saw the beauty around me, the fog and the ocean, rough to the core–but the place I actually have felt most alive.

Arriving home, I pulled off the clothes and stepped into a bath. I remembered taking a bath with Ducu. Then, he had hogged the water, splashing it everywhere, smoked a cigarette and sipped on scotch. That had been a very long time ago, but I remembered only the quality of his skin, a tan smooth skin that seemed resolutely not American in that it was totally sensuous–he was never an "American guy" with tough rawhide skin and light, air-like feelings. No, I'd never been with a man that "exotic" since; he'd been solidly strange and I'd loved it. I stood dripping, the towel around me, the apartment silent. I heard my phone ring a strange sound, not a normal ringtone–it almost sang.

Peter was calling on Facebook. I answered, shivering and exposed.

"Is this okay? To talk?" he pleaded.

"Yes, of course. How are you?"

"I'm so sad, you know. He won't be understood. He's a genius and he's…" Peter collected himself. He sounded as though he were taking a sip of water.

"What time is it there?" I asked.

"Late, but that doesn't matter. I want to make a play about Ducu."

"That's a good idea."

"He tried to help me. He let me make a show at the theater, but they stopped it."

"Who stopped it?"

"They don't want real art there, I wanted to make real art, and once he was sick they…they killed it. They killed me, even though I am sick."

"What are you sick with?"

"My kidney–it was a bad transplant and I tried to help Ducu in the end, and he tried to help me. On the day he died, he was texting me that he loves me…I can show you the texts when I see you, when you come here."

For the months that I had known Ducu was ill, I'd researched care in Romania and was generally appalled at the level of terrible care. As part of the exodus of Romanians to the West, the country had suffered a profound brain drain of doctors, and now, there was corruption, shortages on medicine and horrific care. Some years ago, when Ducu's father fell very ill he had pleaded with me on the phone to never put my parents in a hospital to die. I'd assured him I never would, and he answered, "No, of course not, it's America, I forgot. But here, they just leave you to die. Just promise me!"

Ducu and my mother had loved each other deeply. He would hold her hand when he and I lived in New York together. We would travel the subway to Brooklyn where my mother would make steak and green beans, and she would share a scotch with Ducu and he would ask her about psychiatry. My mother was a family therapist and also an ordained minister–so sometimes he would tease her and call her "doctor"–he liked to do that. He loved to know what made a person, or a character, tick. She's taught me a lot as well, how to listen, how to empathize, how to gather the story of a life and reflect back compassion. But, looking at it now, there are some things she failed to teach me.

Peter was telling me about his health and his love of Ducu. "Ducu told me that you were the love of his life."

"What?"

"Yes, or at least that's what it seemed. That he should never have stayed in Europe."

"I don't think that's right. He made the right decision to be with his family, make art, raise his son…in Europe, he was right."

"You'll see, when you get here. He was wrong. But didn't he have the best smile in the world?"

"Yes."

"That smile was everything. And you must see his *Coriolanus*. Will you?"

"I hope so."

I was suddenly tired. Peter had painted a picture of my fear that Ducu had regrets about me, about his life, that in fact I had made his life difficult when we were young. I asked Peter if we could speak later, turned off the phone, and felt confused.

In the morning, the phone pinged loudly. My WhatsApp was making noise, and it was asking me if I was okay.

"Who's this?" I wrote.

"Me, sunshine." Anya was writing. "You are like sunshine, just as Ducu said."

I stared at the phone. Had he said that about me? That I was sunshine? How could I have forgotten that?

"Send me some of your writing", she said. "I will send it to my friend."

Thumbs Up icon from me.

I spent a good part of the night writing about Ducu. It came out of me as whole piece, about traveling to see him, about the past. Our past. Something I had never written about. Stomach aching, I sent the pages to another actress, a woman who'd befriended me a year before, who'd acted in many of Ducu's plays. I sent her the writing with a question–did she like it?

I put on my pajamas. I got into bed. I slept. I woke.

I opened my email and saw a response from Romania, from the actress whom I liked very much. The email was long, emotional, and pleading with me–do not write this, it said, do not have this published, you will hurt people, you will hurt Ducu's ex-wife; he would not approve. Yet, the message ended, saying that I was the perfect person to write the book, but not this book–not like this, not now. Not while things were so raw.

Raw? What was raw? I sat back shocked. He'd told me to always tell the truth. He'd told me that we were good, that we'd addressed the past–what was going on?

I called Anya and I told her of the email.

"You see, I told you. They are going to try to shut you down, too! She's trying to silence you. She's with *them*. Probably. Send me what you wrote!"

I moved quickly to my computer and shared the writing with her. She read in silence. I waited as I imagined she was reviewing the pages I'd sent.

"But this is beautiful! The world needs to know this. Your True. His True…"

"Truth?"

"No, the True! The real. This is what Romanians are afraid of, hearing about the world they missed out on, and being loved but then failing to love back. It's a romance!"

I hadn't thought of what I'd written as romance. I hadn't thought it was even an attempt at the truth. It was just…what was floating around in me.

"Let me send this to someone, okay? I think I know someone who would want to see this. Ok? May I, please?"

"Sure, if you think so…"

"I know so. Just think about what you want to write and I will stand with you, I will be there for you. I promise. Trust me." And then she hung up.

I sat staring at the screen. I was confused by my response, that I felt such a sense of duty so suddenly, to represent the past. Who gives a shit about me? I thought. This is a book about him? Shouldn't I write a book just about him?

Peter called me. "Hi. I thought I would say hi", he said, calmly.

"Did you talk to Anya?"

"No. What's going on?"

"I got an email from ("actress") and she told me not to write a book…"

"Oh, don't listen to her. She's just jealous. He used to fuck her."

"How do you know that?"

"He told me! They used to have orgies at the theater."

"*What?!*"

"Yes. Romanian actors are sluts. Really, ignore her and keep writing. You have so much to say."

I heard a car backfire and sat upright. I had been friends with "the actress" for a year and she had never mentioned an affair with Ducu. I had poured my heart out to her and she had never mentioned a word. Why was she pleading with me?

"What can I do for you?" Peter asked.

"I guess you could read what I wrote to see if I am off-base."

"Of course! And, I can help you, I can translate for you–articles or interviews. Would that help?"

"That's so kind, yes, thank you!"

"You have to be brave. He's gone now and they will want to control the memory of him."

There it was again. I knew about that–controlling memory. When I was growing up in the theater, and when my father would direct his plays, he used to tell me never to trust critics–their job was to shape your legacy and cut you out of history if they didn't like your work. I had also grown up during the AIDS crisis and had seen our friends waste away and die; and I had seen theaters gone. In Greenwich Village, where my father had his theaters, we saw how death could lead to the collapse of community, to the collapse of memory: theaters closed with no video back then, it was only your memory of the shows, and it was all killed off for us in the 1980s.

Yes, I knew what Peter and Anya were talking about. I'd see this before, and no one was going to shut down Ducu's memory–it was the least I could do.

Yes, I would fight for him.

ACT 2

"Actually, I do happen to resemble a hallucination. Kindly note my silhouette in the moonlight." The cat climbed into the shaft of moonlight and wanted to keep talking but was asked to be quiet. "Very well, I shall be silent", he replied, "I shall be a silent hallucination."

—Mikhail Bulgakov,
The Master and Margarita

Bucharest—December 2019—Arriving

A month before I'd boarded a flight to Romania, I'd received an excited call from Anya.

"I found a publisher!"

"You did?"

"Yes, it is MediaPro Studios. Adrian Sarbu is the CEO and he remembers you from New York."

"New York?"

"Yes, he remembers meeting you with Ducu. You don't remember? He remembers"

"I guess so…"

"Well, he loves what you sent me. He thinks it could be a bestseller–you write about his life but it is exciting as well. He wants to publish it, he wants you to tell all that we don't know about Ducu, all about New York, the secret! And, he wants to publish it in Romania, France, England, and America."

"But it's a movie production company?"

"Yes, Ducu worked with them…but he wants to make books now."

Ducu had told me he'd been involved with some production companies in Romania. I'd had a friend who'd been in a meeting with him twenty years ago. He had directed a lot of television.

"Sarah?"

"Yes?"

"It's great news, right? He has a guy I know well who will help get the contract together. That means you can come here to write about Ducu and I will help you. You can talk to people and tell the True."

I never corrected Anya when she made that mistake of saying "the True" as opposed to telling "the Truth." It was interesting to me, it was as though there were an absolute true-ness to the world that simply had to be uncovered. I understood that feeling, I'd had it earlier in my life as well, how there was a truth to your life that you were in search of–The True–I liked it.

"How will this work?" I asked.

"He will contact you–I gave him your email and he will help get the contract to you. Okay? I think this is great. Come to Bucharest!"

It was October and I had written fifty pages of a book about Ducu. I named it *Ducu Rising*; and I liked the direction, but knew I had to go to Romania to talk to people, to feel the place, to pierce my own fantasies about his culture, even though I'd been there before. I told myself this, that I should not try to "appropriate" his experience–I was being very smart.

Adrian did contact me through a liaison and asked for meetings with me when I would be in Bucharest in December. I accepted, of course, and sent him the first fifty pages.

For the next month, I wrote and wrote. I started to wake up at four-thirty in the morning and write as much as I could. Anya would often call me early in my day to encourage me to keep going. Sometimes, Peter would call and ask to hear how the writing was going–I would read pages aloud and he would give me insights and information: the stories, he said, no one would tell me. They said they loved what I'd written. It meant a lot to me. I kept writing.

November rolled in. I would wake in the early morning, watch the news, the stories of my country colliding with itself. There were more and more school shootings. Trump was being impeached. White supremacists were shouting what they wanted and the Trump government was listening and doing their bidding. We were, many of us in America, glued to the screen to see what daily mess Trump had made. We were living anxiously, it felt, on borrowed time. I kept writing.

At the end of November, I packed my computer with the new book carefully saved, along with my warmest clothes, and my father's advice, "Listen first. Talk later." That was his excited direction, and it was good counsel to not project my ideas, feelings, or desires onto this trip–this one was not chasing romance, this was chasing "The True." I left on a late flight that flew direct from San Francisco to Amsterdam, then on to Bucharest.

When we landed, I gathered my best attitude and my most winning traveling smile and got off the plane. I waited a while for my bags, looking every once in a while at the sliding doors as they opened–people peering in, a bleak cold sky behind them. And then I saw them: Anya and Peter. He was holding flowers and she was looking at me blankly. I walked toward them, realizing in that moment that I did not know them, really, but I was there. Peter looked me up and down, not sexually, but as though I were a strange object from another world. Anya did not smile, she looked struck dumb.

"You…" Anya said. "You look so real in real life."

"What did you expect?" Peter snapped.

"Just…Ducu never told me, she was so…" she stammered.

And there I was in Bucharest, with new friends who were just piecing together that I was real. That I had a face that Ducu had known–that I was other.

"Come now", I urged with a smile, "It is so good to be here. Let's go have some fun!" I was acutely aware in that moment that perhaps they had never met an American, seen how shiny we can be–how we tend to glide into new moments as though we own them. Right? That made sense to me, I should tone it down, not shine so hard and get back to my job, listening.

But, the truth was that I did not like Peter, almost immediately. He had a filminess to him, a kind of misanthropic vibe and I could not picture Ducu being his friend–I could not picture Ducu, well, connected to either of them. Anya was simply not his physical type, he liked women of all forms, but no matter the size he liked a "gamin" quality–a slightness, a close proximity to kinkiness and allure. Anya and Peter had no allure, they were low to the ground–they seemed to move like lost wolves.

That's terrible! I thought to myself. Who am I to judge people in another culture? Perhaps they are just freaked out to meet me? It is one thing to invite people to your home and another to really greet them. Terrible! Focus on listening, I told myself, take it in.

"Let's get this cab", Peter said.

We jumped into a car and Anya was still silent. "I just can't get over what you look like", she said.

I did not know what to say. I felt bad that I was making her uncomfortable.

"Stop, Anya." Peter said, nervously. The cab drove on.

When I was last in Bucharest, it was spring. It had been bright, and flowers were sold in the streets. Now, almost December, a cold fog moved across the city, seemingly freezing the moment I was in. I felt more alone than when I had visited last. Ducu was dead. I was there to find him. Yet these two people felt like absolute strangers, and since I never mind being alone, I wondered if I should not have waited, come in a few months–stayed in my place in America.

"You see these buildings, Sarah?" Peter asked, politely, almost reassuringly, now.

"Yes, it's wonderful", I said, "these old ones to the left."

"They turned them back into museums. But you see in front of us, that's a building I will take you if you like. And also to see where Ceaușescu lived–that's important for you to see."

Anya took my hand. "I'm sorry to be weird", she said. "It's just emotional."

Now that I could see her close up, Anya reminded me of Anna Magnani, the dark and brooding Italian film star of the 1950s. Like Magnani, Anya had deep-set eyes, with slight dark rings under them. Her lips were very full, and her hair, a light brown, sat simply behind her ears. She held her hands together, but looked like she was holding back movement, as though perhaps her fingers might make gestures like Magnani, but she withheld them.

"We're here", said Peter. "This is Anya's apartment building, where you'll be staying." We had stopped on a main boulevard, the cars rushing by, and the cold hit me like a wall when the door was opened on to the street. My bag was pulled to the curb and Peter and Anya watched as I hoisted the luggage up the stairs into the portico. We crammed into a tiny elevator and made our way to the apartment.

The first thing I noticed there were the floors–a stark, natural wood that looked as old as the apartment building, perhaps from the 1920s. Two cats scurried across the floor and zoomed madly into the living room to the right.

"Those are Ducu's cats", Anya said, brightly.

I heard the door slam, heavy, and I took a deep breath. I could not smell him.

"Come in, come in", Anya said, her eyes alert and her body language happy. Peter stood at the door. I walked forward into the living room. "I'm sorry it's so simple", Anya said, taking my bag and putting it by a bright red leather couch with rips in it.

"Not at all, it's very nice."

"Come, look at the view." Anya took my hand, it was now warm and so I squeezed it.

We walked to the window and looked down at the avenue below. She pointed to an apartment building across the street. It was very large and the lights were bright in the windows.

"Ducu lived there when we first met."

I peered at the windows with small balconies. Yes, I remembered him showing me a live image of this very street covered with snow last year. He had turned on FaceTime so I could see his view, his city–this street.

"Yes, I recognize it." I replied to her reflection in the window before us.

"He lived there, that's where I would go. Then, we moved in here, this past year." She turned and pointed at a bed on the far wall in the living room.

"In the end, he slept there. He liked to look out the window." Anya dropped her hand against her thigh and it made a small sound, a thud. "But you must be so hungry or thirsty?"

"I'm okay."

"No, I've made something for you. Peter, come help me get the dishes out."

Anya and Peter left me in the living room. I looked around more carefully. There were many books about the theater on the shelves, along with a Buddha on the wall, and pictures of Ducu with "I love you" in Romanian on them.

Anya re-entered the room with a glass of water.

"Please!" she said, smiling, handing me the glass. "Come eat!"

The kitchen was simple with a bookshelf holding cookies, sweets, chocolate, and bread. There was a small square table where Peter, crouched, was jamming paper under one of the legs to stop it from moving.

"You really need a new table, Anya", Peter scoffed.

"I love that table!"

"It's fucking falling apart."

"It's fine", she said, placing a large pot of stew on the table. "This was his favorite."

It smelled wonderful, and I watched the steam rise up from it. They served me and then themselves. There it was, I thought, there is the Romanian elegance I had known–table manners were always important to Ducu, and everyone I'd met through him ate elegantly, quietly, and with style. But, that soon disappeared.

Peter and Anya slurped the stew. He ate a bit more quietly, but neither moved their napkins to their laps like most Europeans I knew. I thought, you fucking snob, who are you to judge them?

"What would you like to do first?" Anya asked.

"I want to listen", I said.

We sat at the table with its red and white plastic checkered cloth and they began to talk. For at least an hour, they told me how he had suffered. How the theater he ran, the Bulandra Theater, was distancing itself from the memory of him. How, now that I was here, I could talk to people and find out why. I was handed a full mystery, and the writer in me was delighted.

Rising awkwardly, Peter said, "Well, I can tell I am not wanted here anymore." He smiled.

Anya did not disagree. She stood and moved toward his coat in the hall.

"Thank you, Peter." I said, standing as well.

"Don't thank me, just help me with the play I want to write about Ducu. Okay? You can do *that*, right?"

"Sure. Of course. Let's set up some time to do that this week."

"Yes, well, only if you can make the time", he responded, passive-aggressively.

I nodded. He walked to the door. They spoke in Romanian. He left.

Returning to the kitchen, Anya put her hand casually on her waist, saying, "Thank God he's gone! He's such an asshole!"

I burst into laughter because it was true. He was a strange bird, indeed.

"But why are you friends with him if you don't like him?"

"Ducu taught me not to judge. We tried to help him, to be his friend. He was a very good actor, but he got into all sorts of fights with theaters and then he got sick in the kidney. So I try to be kind to him, to understand him."

She took our water glasses and gestured to the living room. We sat on the broken sofa.

"I see there is red in here too?" I asked.

"Yes." She looked around, making no movement in her face.

"Because Ducu loved red. Right?" I offered.

"Oh. Yes, of course. He *loved* red." She touched the sofa.

When I'd talked to Ducu on FaceTime he'd always liked to show me a wall he'd painted red. I think he found it fun or comforting. He was also proud of his CD collection of music. And his books. Books had been our common language. He'd told me last year of a recurring dream about his mother, based on a real moment from his past. When he was thirteen years old, she had taken him into the library, which was filled from floor to ceiling with books. She had stood looking at the books, and had told him that he needed to read with new eyes. He had mentioned this to me, and had wondered if she did that (when he was thirteen) because she was Jewish. I had told him that I thought certainly at thirteen, the age of a bar mitzvah might have been on her mind. Then he changed the subject and we never discussed being Jewish again.

I stood up in Anya and Ducu's apartment and looked at the few books on the shelves.

"I gave a lot of his things away", she said. "Books, clothes, so many things. He meant so much to people."

She stood up and left the room. I went to the one bookcase and saw the works of Chekhov. Yes, he had loved those plays. She returned. She held out her hand, and I saw an earring in her palm.

"This was his. You told me you were with him the first time he got his ear pierced?"

"Yes." I looked at the small, silver stud.

"Please, take this. Put it in your ear so you have something of him."

I held the simple, boring stud between my finger and thumb. I was disappointed. I had really wanted one of his hoops–the large ones that he wore and looked so often like a pirate. But it was not my place to ask for anything of his. It was only my place to listen. I placed the stud in my ear.

"Come with me", she said, and took me into the bedroom. She opened the closet and I saw men's clothing hanging within. "Would you like to smell it?"

"Smell it?"

"Yes. Him."

I stood looking at the clothes. She touched my shoulder. "Let me leave you with him."

I touched the jackets, the fabrics, the scarves–I raised a sleeve to my nose and took in a deep breath. No, these did not smell like him–but I kept trying, I took another deep inhalation and only felt him gone. I backed away from the armoire, I looked at the low bed, a futon, and thought how he must have been uncomfortable on it–but at least he'd had her support.

I remembered being so young when I first met him in London. That summer of 1990, I discovered yoga and I would meditate and practice the ancient tradition every morning. I had a sense of who I was for the first time in my life, and in the context of great change–the fall of the Berlin Wall and a "new Europe" on the horizon–I had hoped to not return to America, I hoped for a new life in an old country. So when Ducu and I met we both had been set free by history, and both of us rebelled against the Royal Court Theater that was eager to promote international artists, but still lived in the memory of British playwrights from the 1960s. I had practiced my yoga and he had directed in the top of the theater at "the Court." Aware we still weren't free, we struck up a friendship and then a romance. Perhaps it was his cologne? Ducu seemed to embrace everything new and fashionable in record time, dousing himself with cologne that wafted through the halls of the theater. I could find him anywhere, I could sniff and I was led to where he was, always with a cigarette, always talking with an artist, almost always laughing. His smell led me through dark passageways in many theaters to come, and into dark places within me that year and then into my adult life: his smell, a phantom, never left my side.

I took one last deep inhalation and still could not find him. So I went to the living-room. Anya was sitting on the couch. She had pulled off her bra which now lay on a chair. Her breasts were enormous under her shirt. I was trying not to stare. I was also trying not to imagine what Ducu had done with them. Stopping myself, I smiled and looked at her face. She was sweet, now. She was calm, and she took my hand.

"Now", she said, tenderly. "We are sisters."

That night, I went to bed in the living-room. I slept in the bed where he had spent his last days. I searched for him in the sheets. I assumed, now with nothing left of him but shadow, that he had moved on from me, that he had died with her, and thank God, he had not been alone. Yes, she was my little sister, a person who loved him better than I could. Yes, I fell asleep in that cold room and tried not to think of his hands.

The True: Part One

Beginning in the 1990s, Ducu and Maria took the world by storm. Creative partners, the couple had been "discovered" in London for their production of *A Midsummer Night's Dream* and then traveled the world. Maria is small, elegant, and very gamine, like a Parisian film star of the 1920s. In Bucharest, they were considered a treasure. For decades, Ducu had always said Maria understood the depths of him, that she was good, and kind, and that he had been a shit.

For decades, I'd watched as they made work together and built a repertoire of theater that dazzled. There was nothing they would not try together, and she was, in the end, the woman everyone said knew him best. I was looking forward to trying to connect with her; though nervous, I'd been told by many of my Romanian friends in the United States and in Bucharest that I really should reach out to her, out of respect.

"I have bad news for you", Anya told me the next morning. "I did not want to upset you in America, but it is not good."

I set down my coffee, the steam heat having dried up the air in the apartment. Parched, I raised my eyebrows.

"It's Maria. She does not want you to write a book."

"What? How would she know."

"She heard you were in town and called everyone, I mean everyone, and told them not to talk to you."

I was struck dumb. It had been thirty years since I had any relevance to Maria. I'd hoped to explain the vision of the book, to share how it explored the place of the feminine and women in Ducu's life–she was essential to the research.

"I don't understand."

"What is so hard to understand?" Anya said, cooly. "You are his past and she wants only his theater to be remembered."

"But that's what I want to do!"

"No, you are writing about his past with *you* in America."

"I don't have to do that."

"Look, that's what the publisher wants–the truth about his private life."

"It's not my place to write about his private life."

"Are you afraid?"

"What?"

"You are afraid to write his truth? You think she would allow that?"

"Why don't I call her now and see what's wrong?"

"No! You have to trust me. I am friends with their son, Anton–he would tell you to just let it go. She hates me, too, which makes me so sad because I grew up with her."

"You did? How?"

"I was often at their house when I was a kid. They took care of me and I was too wild and she tried to tame me, but I couldn't be tamed. I was wild!"

"So you know her. Let's call and I can explain."

"You don't know her when she is angry! She is fierce and she has already called all the theaters and there is a ban on you. They won't talk to you. You'll have to find another way. Don't worry, my sister", she said, taking my hand, "I will help you."

I looked at my laptop sitting alone on the bed. I'd planned the interviews. I had questions and had already researched the Teatrul de Comedie where

Ducu had grown up. I had no idea what to do. She must have seen that in my eyes.

"Look. I have many friends who loved Ducu and they will talk to you. All of them. Come, get dressed. Let's go to a nice restaurant and meet Summer. She was his friend forever, she was at the theater for forty years, she was Liviu Ciulei's assistant for years. She knows so much. Come, get dressed."

I put on my clothes and wrapped an extra layer around me, then pulled on my parka.

Returning from her room dressed and holding a large scarf, Anya said, "This was his. You will be warm with it."

I pulled the scarf around my throat, smelling for him, but no, nothing but the scent of a long lost perfume. The door made a heavy thud as we exited. She took my hand.

We walked three short blocks to a restaurant on the corner. The day was uniquely gray, and the cars moved quickly past people on bicycles. We walked up the steps out of the cold and into the hip restaurant. "This place was his favorite", she whispered into my ear.

The waiter led us to a table and placed a menu before me. I searched for a pasta and Anya looked for some meat. We waited for Ducu's friend called Summer. Anya told me she was old, cool, and one of the few people Ducu had loved at the end of his life. Summer was like "a sister" to him. I had never heard of her, but would be grateful to meet her.

Summer arrived dressed in black, wearing an asymmetrical haircut, earrings up and down her ears, Tibetan bracelets, and shiny rings. I stood to greet her and she threw her arms around me with tears in her eyes. "He told me so much about you!" she said.

Summer sat across from me and held my hands, tightly. Her eyes were marvelous, alive and kind. She looked at me, warmly, and began to speak in broken English. Finally, she turned to Anya and said, "But, you translate."

Summer started to speak in Romanian. She was clearly moved by what she was saying and she took my hands again, then wiped tears from her eyes. Anya slowly translated, but her English did not seem to match the emotions before me.

"You understand me?" Summer pleaded.

I did not. But, there was time. Summer was clear that she wanted to help me with the book. She told me, through Anya, that she would help any way she could, and that the theater he had run was "going down"–that it was lost, that when you went into the theater now, "it is like the sky waiting for rain."

I loved Summer. She was a real theater person, the kind I'd grown up with who loved to be part of a crew, a family, and had the capacity to listen to the same show over and over while managing it technically. I had a feeling she wished she could be alone with me. But how would we have understood each other?

Summer continued, translated by Anya, "He was so like his mother! He could sense the world of a person, he could feel everything. And in this way had the problem of feelings." She explained, "He was the person that you loved immediately, though quickly it became clear that you would never really possess him as a person or an artist, and then people would feel an anger, a loss, and then came the jealousy. People could be so cruel towards him, so many people did not understand. They could be very ugly."

"Who was ugly?" I urged.

"The world. The theater. People", she said.

The ugliness of people in the art world is a universal story, not specific to Romania or Ducu. Artists of merit often deal with the jealousy of others, but Ducu, who'd had a skill set that was not fully formed, was motivated to keep creating in the face of competition, yet often he believed the bullshit he was sold, the negative reinforcement or overt lies to make him lose faith in himself. Artists often have this trait–listening to negative voices on the outside and from within. Directors have it especially hard, for they must be deeply confident yet have a reasonable degree of doubt in order not to explode within their egos.

If you were to live in the head of most directors, you would find an equal amount of negative self-talk and self-congratulation, the negative voices often winning the conversation. Directors must manage this self-talk, their own and those of the artists they work with. “Come now”, I once heard him say to an actor, “that’s what you think of you, but what does the character think of himself?” It was a twenty-four hour, non-stop game to trick the brains of company members into playing pretend, making a new world, and building a mirage on a stage.

It is also true that theaters are fabulously dangerous places in general, but in Romania the Machiavellian nature of theater is epically alive and well: it’s a combination of ancient secrets and alliances protected by the remains of Communist threat and innuendo. How he managed the level of emotional war-play in the theater amazes me. Truth is, there were many people in Ducu’s life who often wanted him to tone down his talent, to make space for them to shine, to not be too fabulous. When he was young, beautiful, and daring the world to take him on, he fought rather well against the envy. Yet later, as he grew older, not even the women whom he trusted could protect him from his own belief in the negative words of others.

And this is particularly sad because Ducu was a fantastic friend. Even though he was never on time, he was never late for friendship. He followed his heart completely with friends, giving support or funds, professional help or personal attention. Every person close to him speaks of his generosity, his ability to feel with you, his ability to remember your details. Yet over the years, Ducu began to find it hard to say no to people, and this could get him into trouble, a tight space with those who perhaps did not have the best intentions.

Listening to Summer, I was suddenly struck by how sad it was that Consuela was no longer alive, that she had left the scene so early in the 1980s, leaving Ducu without the reason and calm of her presence. He had talked about longing for her, for her sweetness, her familiar eyes. So he searched, I believe, in women. His friends, colleagues, lovers–he was always looking for the place of beauty where he'd be accepted for himself and encouraged to be fully alive. Ducu spent a good part of his life looking the world over for her memory in others. Yet he could not find her, and perhaps he turned to a bottle filled with a toxin capable of making him forget he'd not accomplished his search. For a time, he sucked at the tit of booze at parties with models–their beauty completely intoxicating–after rehearsals and at late night parties with friends who drank, the world quiet without her.

In the end, Ducu thought he was wrong about things even though he was victorious in the theater–every new play a cause célèbre, every new story an example of his talent–except, deep down, he never felt he had hit the mark.

These thoughts overwhelmed me in the restaurant with the two women I had just met. How in the end Ducu had not believed he would be remembered. How, perhaps, in the end, this is the fear we all have.

Then, a plate of pasta and a thin broiled steak was brought to the table, and Anya ate, hungrily. She then set down her fork and started to cry.

"Oh, what will I do without him!" she cried, leaning into Summer's arm resting beside her. Summer looked at me, and I thought, for just a second, that she rolled her eyes.

"You will see *Coriolanus*?" Summer asked me.

"Yes, right before I go home."

Summer nodded to Anya who was wiping her tears with a now dirty napkin. Anya translated. "You will see. He was a genius, and no one understood that. He was a person of deep feelings, like his mother, someone who understood what was not being said. And they could be so cruel, so mean to him–they did not understand those feelings he had, they did not understand anything."

Summer smiled at me. I smiled back.

"Yes, but…" Anya said to Summer in English, "You both could be so disgusting with each other!"

"Well, he and I had a funny jokes with each other–we liked to tease."

Yes, when Ducu loved you, he joked a lot. I smiled again at Summer, her fingers now overlapping, her elbows off the table. I imagined that she was once a real beauty. Earlier, walking to the restaurant, Anya had said Summer had also been a famous mistress to the theater men of Bucharest. I had no reason not to believe her; that's also a part of the theater, a role many women played through history.

"You should try to talk to Maria", Summer said.

Turning toward Summer, Anya said something in Romanian. The women had an animated conversation. Summer seemed to protest. Anya carried on.

"I'm sorry", Anya told me, "I had to explain to her what is going on. She is shocked."

"I am shocked!" said Summer. "Maria is wonderful, I don't understand."

"Summer, what do you think is most important that I know about Ducu?" I said.

Stopping, Summer looked me in the eye, saying, "That without him, there may be no Romanian theater left. He took it all. He took it with him."

At that, Anya smiled.

The waiter came. He gave me the bill. I paid it. Summer thanked me. Anya took a dark black roll and bit it, hard.

We left the restaurant after an hour. Summer walked in front of me, limping and using a cane. We walked only halfway up the block when we arrived at Summer's home. It was hard to see the house because there was only a door inserted into a metal wall. She opened the door and I saw a small garden. She turned, kissed me, and whispered, "Remember, he loved you." And then she winked, waved, and closed the door.

As we walked towards another restaurant for coffee, Anya's phone rang. She spoke in Romanian, quickly and quietly. She hung up, smiled, and said Peter would meet us for coffee.

"He really wants to see you and he got tickets for something for you both. I think you should go with him, he really believes you need to see the house of Ceaușescu to understand Ducu's story."

"Sure, I think it sounds interesting. But I don't think Ducu would have seen the palace. Right? It was closed."

"He just wants to give you something special", Anya said, waving her hand. "He's a lonely guy, you mind?"

I shrugged. The liaison for the publisher had written me before I left saying that he wanted me to really take in Bucharest, feel it, experience it so I could write about it. I agreed in the abstract, and now, walking in the freezing cold to another place to sit, I seemed to have no choice.

The restaurant was small and they served Anya a hot chocolate as thick as soup. It reminded me of the hot chocolate in Paris, a kind of luscious event you needed to sip for hours.

"They have this in Paris", I said to Anya.

She grinned. "I love it! It's so smooth. I had this with Ducu in Paris when we were there for his treatments."

"When was that?"

"Last year. We flew there and nobody knew."

"What was it for?"

"The same help we looked for in Istanbul. You see, he never wanted help, but then he let me help him. I mean, I can get pretty crazy, pretty serious when I need to. He told me that I can be like a gypsy, or like a Jew. I can make anything possible."

This insight took me aback. "Like a Jew" lingered in the air. I looked at Anya again. I wondered what her heritage was.

"Are you Roma?" I asked her.

"I have no idea."

"Why?"

"Because I was adopted."

"Really?"

"Yes, but I didn't find out until I was eighteen. They told me by mistake, my parents. Then I looked for my mother and I found her. I went to her house, to her door and I knocked…"

Ayna looked down at her hands. She looked at me again with tears in her eyes. "I was shocked. I told her who I was. I told her I was her child. But she walked away from me, like she did not even know who I was. It destroyed me. That's why Ducu was so important to me, he always believed me, he was always kind. Not like my real mother. I hate her now. She made it impossible for me to love her–and myself."

I felt her vulnerability, deeply. Yes, I knew there had been a law during Ceaușescu's rule that abortions were illegal. But, that was in the 1980s.

"How old are you, Anya?"

"I'm thirty-three."

I did the math in my head. Yes, perhaps that added up. She was born before the revolution.

"My father was in the military. And they lived in Bucharest. My parents had wanted to save a little baby from one of those places–all the babies, all alone."

"So they saved you?"

"Yes, I suppose they did. But you know, they lived in the same building with Ducu when he was a little boy."

"Really?"

"Yes, they lived there and saw how wild he was. He was a wild child, too. Very sweet, but very wild. That's why we understood each other."

"So, how do you know Maria so well?"

"I was a little kid, well, more like a teenager, and I was their son's best friend for a very long time. And I grew up in their home."

At that moment, Peter walked in. Dressed in blue jeans, he also wore a large ring he immediately told me was Ducu's. Greeting us, nervously, he sat down and ordered a coffee.

Peter and Anya did not greet each other. They never kissed cheeks. They never touched. But when they sat together there was always a conversation about Ducu about to take place. I quickly began to see the pattern, that they needed to share something with me–but that somewhere they did not agree and on a fundamental topic, who did Ducu love more, Anya or Peter.

We sat for a long time at that table. We ate some mussels and fries. We discussed plans for the next day when I would go with Peter to see Ceaușescu's house in the city. Drained by the end, I listened though all I heard was bad news–that the theater was over; there was a conspiracy of silence; I would have to dig very deep to write anything–real.

The next day, Peter arrived promptly. He waited downstairs and Anya prepared me for the day. But before I left, I received a text on WhatsApp from Anton–Ducu's son. "I hear you are here. I wanted to say hi. Let's talk." Astounded, I responded that I was thrilled to hear from him, and that I wanted to talk with him.

Closing the door behind me, Anya said, "Try to have fun."

In the cab on the way to the "palace", Peter asked me a very direct question: "What do you think of Trump?"

"I think he's dangerous."

"But isn't he rich?"

"Perhaps."

"But he knows what to do with money. He can run a business?"

"I don't think that has been proven."

"But he's really rich. I saw his valet who is Romanian on a TV show and he loved him. He said he was a great boss."

"That may be so, but that does not mean he's a good president."

"But he's trying hard to get the blacks to behave."

"Sorry?"

"He's going to do something about the blacks. It's a problem. They are a problem."

I looked out the window at Bucharest in the cold. It was consistently gray. It was filled with people trying to stay warm. Their government was constantly in flux, they had not known any stability since 1989. I took a deep breath and tried to understand where Peter was coming from.

"Peter, what would you like from your government?"

"Want? What is there to want? They are crooks and thieves and you can't trust any of them. Just like all the politicians before. No, perhaps it was better under Ceaușescu. We might not have had heat, but we had a point of view. Now it's nothing, lots of nothing with people on their phones, not going to the theater, not talking to one another–we are lost."

The taxi pulled up to a building.

"Look around. You will see lots of beautiful buildings here. But during Ceaușescu this was all closed off, just for him, just so he could be safe."

We exited the cab and walked into a large villa. We were greeted at a front desk, and Peter showed them tickets he had purchased weeks before. Then we were led into a small room and given paper booties to place over our shoes. We waited, quiet, in a room with golden wallpaper.

A woman brought us into the first parlor, the place where the Communists, both Russian and Romanian, would hold meetings. This was the first area of the house. Peter pointed at a Soviet-style phone attached to a large recording device. "Amazing isn't it?" I nodded, politely.

We moved through each room on the first floor. Brown room after brown room, one hard, varnished chair after another. The tour guide would point out the antiques–few were actually real, replicas, though, given to Elena Ceaușescu to make her home "elegant." We entered one of the large dining rooms, the linen was set and the china was arranged as though the couple would soon arrive for dinner. And in the center of the room was an enormous,

1960s-style television–Soviet brand with an enormous clicker on the table. To the right of the television was a round table, set for the next breakfast.

"And here is the breakfast nook. Ceaușescu was sick his whole life, so there was always healthy food and a doctor to see him through his day. He always had medicine." The guide moved towards the next room.

Peter nodded, sadly. "He always had medicine. He was smart. But you see he was sick. It's amazing he could do as much as he did."

The entire first floor felt like a tomb, its frozen falseness simply freaking the shit out of me.

We followed the tour guide up a large set of stairs. Walking up halfway, Peter said, "Wow, this is huge!" Pulling out his phone, he asked me to snap a shot of him. He looked at the photo I took, he smiled, and placed the phone back in his pocket. I felt my phone ding. Pulling it out, I saw Anton was writing to me.

"Why are you there?" Anton wrote.

"It was a friend who brought me here."

"Who?"

"Peter."

"Him?! But, that guy, I hope Anya is showing you a proper time! I am in the mountains, but I will be back soon. I hope it's okay. It's very strange to bring you there!"

I had to agree with Anton. But at this point we were in the Ceaușescus' main bedroom, which was full of white and yellow faux-French linen. Their clothes were still laid out on the bed. Peter took many pictures of this room, and then we moved to the closets, where their brown and gold lamé clothing still hung. So many shoes there. Feeling sick to my stomach, I remembered the photos of Imelda Marcos, the wife of the dictator of the Philippines, and her thousands of shoes.

"Wow!" Peter said. "This is amazing."

I took a deep breath.

We walked down more stairs toward a spa for the family–large vats to soak in, a full doctor's examination room, and an excess of machines to trim any fat. Further on, we found a pool, enormous with huge windows and mosaics everywhere. It was stunning and horrifying–it was tacky and exceptionally soviet–it was, all of it, a testament to bad taste and greed.

"I've never seen anything so beautiful", Peter said. "I am going to bring my parents here. So, did you like it?"

We were now standing in the "garden", a flat space with peacocks running about.

"Why don't I take another picture of you?" I said. Smiling, broadly, he handed me his phone. I took his picture in the garden that smelled of death. He posted it online.

"Shall we eat?" he asked, cautiously.

Walking to an Italian restaurant, we sat and ordered coffee.

How was it I had never discussed this place with Ducu? Perhaps because he could not have cared less. He hated Ceaușescu with his whole being. He'd told me stories of growing up within the dictatorship and always, whenever he mentioned it, he would shiver. I Had know that he and Maria had suffered terribly, that his friends had been tortured and killed, that people in his life had disappeared–no, he would never have mentioned this place, a home for the corrupt.

"I really will bring my parents here. They can see what a big, beautiful house looks like. They have just grown up only in small apartments. But, for you, as an American, this must be nothing!"

"We have large houses yes, but that was…very specific to the time."

"Time of what?" he demanded.

"A time of totalitarianism."

"Why do you say that?"

"Excuse me?"

"Totalitarianism. Why do you say that?"

"Because it was."

"Says who? The West? America? Perhaps it is just our history."

"Of course." I backed away from the impasse, but he would not let go.

"I mean, look at us now. We have things, all sorts of things, phones, clothes, computers, you name it. We have everything, but we have nothing."

"That's true around the world…consumerism."

"No, it's not the same! I went to England. Ducu told me I had to travel. He told me I had to go to Liverpool, because I love the Beatles. I went there right before he died. I wore a shirt…wait, I will show you."

Peter showed me a photo of him wearing a picture of Ducu on his shirt. "I wore that shirt to England and I had someone take a picture and send it to him. It was amazing in England–I had never been away from Romania, ever–and I saw where Paul and John were from. But, my god, the travel to get there was horrible! It was filled with ugly Romanians and gypsies, filled with the worst of this country. I was so ashamed. I didn't want to return to Romania, but then I saw all the blacks they had in England and realized it's not safe anywhere. So,

I came home, but Ducu died before I could see him. He texted me from the hospital. He…"

Peter picked up his coffee and I had the feeling he felt he'd said too much. I did not know what to do–I could not talk politics, I could not share his enthusiasm for the "palace" and I could sense he needed to be Ducu's favorite–I was exhausted.

We took a taxi back to Anya's. I tried to give Peter a kiss on the cheek, but he pulled away. I had, I felt it, disappointed him–I had not understood his tour, I had not accepted his ideas. Pulling away, I hoped I wouldn't have to see him again.

In the apartment, Anya waited with a bottle of wine open.

"How was it? Bad?"

"Oh god, I can't even tell you."

"I told him not to take you there. It's a very strange place to want to take a guest. Really strange."

"It was truly a creepy place."

Pausing, she gulped some wine, then looked at me, coolly.

"But, tell me the truth, do you hate this apartment?"

"What?" I felt like I was in danger.

"Peter told me you hate it here, that it's too common for you."

"I never said that!"

"He said so, and that you are a beautiful face, that men have loved you, like Marilyn Monroe, but you're…well, spoiled."

I didn't know what to say. I was speechless. And I was hurt.

"Well, never mind! I have invited someone wonderful over who *really* knew Ducu. She's a director and was the student of Ciulei. She's coming by. You know her? Cleo?"

Deeply inhaling, I closed my eyes, then opened them, exhaling. "No, I don't know her."

"She's great. Have some wine and relax."

We waited for an hour and a half and Anya drank most of the wine. She was starting to slur her words when the doorbell rang. Cleo stood, slight and impish in the doorway. She removed her shoes and I saw she was wearing funny socks–I liked her immediately.

Cleo held out her arms and hugged me. She was lively, wonderfully dressed in Asian clothes, and smiled with her whole face. "He told me about you!" she whispered, holding me close. "He told me how much you meant to him."

I pulled back. Reflexively, and not because of anything she had done–I just pulled back.

Anya led us to the living room again and we sat. Cleo held my hand.

"I was in his office one time when you called. His face lit up. He was so happy to hear from you."

"Oh, that's very kind. He never…"

"He was kind of mysterious, yes? But, my English is so bad! I want to say, *private*. That's what I want to say."

Anya poured herself more wine. And then, as though we had missed a cue in a play, she began to weep. Loudly, with big tears running down her face. Cleo held my hand tighter. We looked at each other.

"There, there…" Cleo said to Anya.

"How will I live without him?" Anya lay back on the couch and sobbed. "How? How long will this pain last?"

Cleo and I looked at each other. She tried to learn forward to tell me something and Anya wailed again. "How will I live without *my* Ducu?"

Now I have seen some plays written by Chekhov, but I had never been *in* this play–though this was not Moscow that this "Masha" was longing for, but for a man, a dead man. Numb, I felt like a member of an audience. Holding my hand, Cleo touched my face, and whispered, "This must be so hard for you?" In a flash, I felt seen, respected, and then I felt nothing, again.

Cleo told me she loved Ducu as a brother and felt his care and protection. She expressed to me, though, that the lesson she learned from Ducu was how to become a leader. "He told me to start by being inspired and that what I have inside is enough." She paused, pensively. "'Just be relaxed,' he told me, 'and then people will be inspired.'"

I asked her if Ducu was a typical Romanian.

"No. He was from everywhere."

Anya started weeping again. I awaited a scene change, some lights to shift, a sound effect to arrive. But nothing, just more of Anya convulsively crying.

Finally, Cleo stood up to leave. At the door, she pulled me to her, saying, "I want to see you again. Please, I want to talk to you–this must be so hard. Remember, he loved *you*."

Cleo smiled at me warmly, and left. Anya, very, drunk lay on the couch. Walking to the kitchen, I got a loaf of bread. Anya had drunk all the wine with no food. I also grabbed a bottle of water.

"Hey, lady", I said. "You really need to eat something."

Anya apologized, profusely. She was sorry she drank. She was sorry for her outburst. But, she needed to feel.

"Sometimes, I feel like a robot", she said. "I feel like I can't get out from where I am. I know that means I have problems, but you see, Ducu knew how to talk to me. Sometimes, it all just comes out, my true, my real feelings. And so thank you, thanks for being kind to me!"

The house was warm with her tears.

The sofa was ripped and broken.

I was alone in Romania, and I wasn't sure I was going to have any material–of my own–to write this book.

"Anya, I think for the next couple of days I should write and we should try to talk to some people. Yes? I think I need…"

"But you have everything…"

"No. I really need Maria. I really do."

"But she hates you."

"Well, I don't know that."

"I do! She hates you."

"That's not how life works…we change, things change. I need to meet her."

"One moment!" Anya jumped to her feet, ran toward her room. "I hear my phone!"

I hadn't heard a thing. Returning, she held the phone before her like it was a weapon. She looked at it and then at me.

"Anton", she said. "He tried to kill himself!"

THE TRUE – PART TWO – 2019

(There should have been a scene change here. If Ducu had lit this scene a cherry red spotlight would have hit her face, and Anya, with hand clenching her phone high in the air, would have continued on without pause. I sat shaking on the red couch.)

"He tried to kill himself because he was ashamed. He wanted to meet you but it's too much, too painful. He thinks you ruined his father's life."

I gawked at Anya, having no idea what she was talking about.

"And, he needs money."

I could not feel my body. My breathing was shallow. I was so tired. I was aware that the fog outside was freezing and creeping over the city.

I started to cry.

Anya looked at me, coolly, warmth slowly flowing into her eyes.

"What's wrong?" she said, placing her hand on my shoulder. "He will be okay. It's okay. We just need to help him..."

"I hurt him?"

"Ducu told him you were weak."

"Weak?"

"Yes."

"But, I was just a kid when I was with him. We became such deep friends. Ducu said we were good."

"Let's just have compassion for Anton. Can you help him?"

"What's going on?"

"He drove into a car."

"What?"

"Yes. And now he needs some money for the hospital. It's a private one so we have to pay."

"Why doesn't he have..."

"They stole the wallet."

"Let's call Maria."

"No! She will be furious."

Spent, I could barely move. I had the instinct to call my father back in America.

Anya got back on her phone and texted Anton.

I picked up my phone and called my father.

"He what?!" my father said, loudly.

"He tried to kill himself. Because of me."

"You? What's this about?"

"It's a lot."

"Look, let me send some money to you, but I want you to make sure to get some rest or something. Can you write?"

Constantly on the go, I hadn't written since I arrived. I seemed to be walking in a dream, but not one with a through line.

"I haven't written."

"You need to. Write it all down."

"I have too much coming at me."

"Keep listening. But I'm sending you some money. Use it as you wish. Okay?"

My father, a tough kid from Brooklyn, has always been fond of crazy. In his theaters, he was known to work well with people who were slightly off beam, and he could get amazing performances from even the most looney. I'd grown up with the eccentric, the emotional, and the wild at heart. I'd seen how, deep down, artists were simply trying to reconcile one loss or another. Ducu was the same, he could see the pattern of the person before him, speak to their heart, and give them the space to make art of their feelings. I knew "expression" when I saw it, I knew I was in some kind of expressive blow-out, but I was in Romania, alone, and I simply had to see it through.

Turning to Anya, I said, "Let's go to the bank."

"What, why?"

"Because I will give Anton money to get care."

"But you don't have to do that!"

"I can. I will."

"He will be so emotional–this is so nice. Let me tell him."

She texted him. Then I heard my phone ping. It was Anton, thanking me in a text.

"Come, let's go to the bank." At least I could help Anton.

Anya and I dressed and made our way to an ATM. I got money. I handed it to her. She deposited it into her bank. She pulled out her phone and sent Anton money. We walked away, and the matter was never mentioned again.

Over the next few days, we met with many people–designers, actors, and a few friends. None of the people I really needed to speak with made themselves available. Peter told me he had reached out to Teatrul de Comedie and they did not return the call. I tried to problem-solve on my own, but privately wondered why and who could possibly care about me, my voice. This needed to be about

Ducu–but I was left only with my memories, and that's where I was stuck.

One night, Peter insisted we go to Ducu's theater to see *Art*, a show that had been on Broadway for years. Written by Yasmina Reza, the play was about friends fighting over the relevance of a painting that one of them had bought. It's a very "talky" play and in Romanian it was almost impossible to understand. Yet there is a trick to watching actors. If an actor is really good, you can understand their story through their body, especially their hands, which will inform the feelings, inform the narrative arc of each scene.

Before we went into the theater, Peter and I had stood in the cold waiting for Anya. Tapping my shoulder, Peter had walked me around the corner. Gasping, I'd seen an enormous picture of Ducu I had taken in the early 1990s in the window.

"But, how…"

"You took this picture?"

"Yes."

"Let me take a picture of you with the picture."

"No, I'm not comfortable with that."

"Please." And he quickly took a picture with my face reflected in the photograph. I looked at the picture again.

"But they must know I took that…"

"Sure."

"Then why won't they talk to me?"

"Fuck them", he said, and walked toward the main door. Anya greeted us, and when we went into the main foyer she pointed at a picture of Liviu Ciulei, the great master director who had run the theater, and who had later tapped Ducu to continue his work.

"You see", Anya said, "They have Ciulei up on the wall but not Ducu."

I was impressed by how full a house there was and how people chatted with excitement to enter the theater. As we entered, I was struck by the royal blue hall. There was not a spot of red, the usual color of a theater, anywhere. No, Ducu had decided it needed to be blue, and with some controversy, had changed the hue while also lining the hall with state of the art lighting that I'd seen only on Broadway.

Watching *Art*, the people listened and laughed. I checked the theater for ghosts. Longing for Maria, I wished I could speak with her about them. Looking to the side of the stage, I imagined Ducu there, a ghost, translucent and alive. Dazed, I thought of how all over the world theater artists like to put a table in the front rows of a theater as they integrate the lights and costumes to a play. I imagined Maria and

Ducu sitting at that table for so many productions. I imagined them talking about the work. I imagined them, the life they built, the life they made, and I was in awe. Yes, theaters are the same everywhere, and I missed her, and I missed him, tremendously.

I imagined Ducu's mother, elegant and beautiful, moving among actors long gone. I imagined Ducu, sitting in this theater, watching this stage he knew too well, and wondered if he had missed her too. Had he whispered to her ghost just as he whispered to others in theaters around the world? Had he seen her in shadows? Had he remembered her voice? The Bulandra was a place of history, now his history, and I was a member of its audience wondering about anything but the play performed in front of me. I did not understand a word of *Art*, but I was finally safe in a theater. I was also deeply alone. And, so, words came to me. I started to write in my head. I did not have paper, so I put ideas into my phone. I could breathe in his theater. I could smell him. I could feel, feel myself.

When it was over, I saw that both Peter and Anya were crying, and it hit me, my god, they were sentimentalists. Peter, who'd seen this play over and over again, was a loner searching a play for friendship. Anya, wiping the wet from her eyes, took my hand and stated, saccharine, "I *miss* him."

I wanted to go home. I missed California. I missed my family. We stood as the lights came up. Anya said, "Let's go back and say hello to the actors."

We walked to the door leading backstage and went through the halls to the dressing rooms.

"I know them well", Anya said.

But the actors seemed to look past us. One of the leading men grabbed his coat and walked away. Another stood at his door and smiled, politely. The other leading man motioned for Anya to come toward him–they spoke, animated, then he left, too. I did not meet them. Sad to be there, I was ready to sleep.

In the dark city, the cabs not stopping, Anya took my hand again and led us toward a bus stop. We waited for the bus. Peter left on his own. "You must be tired", Anya said.

"Yes."

"And, I'm sorry if you can't understand the words of the play, but it was very good."

"I'm sure."

The bus came. We entered it. We stood as the bus bobbed along the street.

"You know, that actor was mad at me."

Nothing surprised me now. I was getting used to the storyline. I was submitting to the drama.

"Really?"

"Yes, he didn't know why I was with Peter."

"Why?"

"Because of what Peter did to Ducu."

"And that was?"

"He reported him to the government."

(*What the fuck was wrong with these people? I mean really, what?)*

"What?"

She put her hand on my shoulder. "I think I made a mistake."

(You think?)

"Okay, what was it?"

"I should not have gone there with Peter. He reported Ducu to the municipality when Ducu would not help him with a show. So that actor was mad at me. I'm sorry I could not introduce you, he was just so mad."

I was deeply tired. It was days into a ten-day visit and I was in need of rest. When we got to the apartment, I wanted to fall deeply asleep. I did not want to dream. I did not have to, the evening had been a nightmare. I wanted to be alone, but that was not to be. Anya came into the living room and sat on the bed.

"You are so brave to be here."

"I don't know about that."

"Yes, you are. You really loved him. You really came here two times to see him, once alive and once dead. That means a lot. I hope someone loves me like that one day."

"I hope so, too."

"I think I need to understand myself better. I think you help me understand that, and I want to thank you. I think to really focus on being a director, to really take all he taught me and do a good job."

"That's wonderful. Yes, you should focus. Really find your voice, your passion."

"Yes. Here it's all about men, what they want, never what we want."

"Hmmm…"

"And you know, when my husband almost beat me to death, bashed in my head…"

"What?"

"Yes, I was married and he broke my head. I nearly died. I have never really been able to see straight again. I think that made it hard for me, made trusting hard for me. I went to see a therapist here, and she was really great. She told me I could not attach to people. Then, she left the country to work elsewhere. I wish I had someone to talk with here."

Looking at Anya, I saw the little girl she was describing, frightened, alone, and aware she was not whole. Kissing my hand, she said, "See, like Ducu. He always kissed a person's hand. I kiss your hand." And then, she left.

Opening up my email in Facebook, I saw a note from a pretty famous actor in Bucharest. I'd had an email exchange with him about Ducu's death when, at that time, emotions had been high and I had exchanged with a lot of emotional strangers. He was a very nice person, and for some reason I trusted him. I told him I was in Bucharest. He asked me to dinner. He was handsome. He was charming. I said yes.

The next evening, I prepared for the dinner, and Summer came over to give me some jewelry she had made for me. I put makeup on, did my hair, and longed for a good conversation with a man I thought would know how to pour a woman a glass of wine.

"Be careful with him", Anya said.

"Why?" I said.

"He fucks everything."

"I don't think dinner means I will fuck him", I said, trying on another shirt.

"But he will want that."

"I'm an American. It does not mean that for me." I didn't care if I was being a bitch, I just wanted a night away from Anya.

"You should be careful!" Summer said.

These women were from another planet. Looking at them, I put on my tight army fatigue pants and left with my jacket slightly open for the night.

I met the actor at a restaurant where I'd met everyone. There was a wrap party for a film happening, and the actors looked at me, and I looked back at them–a wrap party is the same in any part of the world, it was familiar. Feeling someone touch my shoulder, I turned around. He was there, looking at me, and he said, "Wow!" Suddenly, I felt different, slightly exposed. I walked to his car, got in, and asked him to drive.

"Where do you want to go?" he asked, smooth and elegant. Just like I like it.

"Anywhere. Just a drive, perhaps some food?"

"Of course." And then he did just that; he drove through Bucharest at night–explaining the city, telling me about the buildings, and then he parked in front of a restaurant. We walked in, and he took my coat. He ordered for us, and then, thank god, he poured me a glass of wine. We talked politics, we talked theater, we talked film, we talked about his childhood and then his love of Robert De Niro.

Then, he let me know he needed to return to the party, it was his wrap party, and I smiled. He made no advance but I asked him, "Why did you reach out to me?"

"It's Facebook. I try to have a real relationship with people."

"Is that possible?"

"I don't know. Is this real?"

"Sure."

"But, I will tell you, I can get addicted and I did have to leave Facebook, because I'm a flirt and I get in trouble." He smiled.

"What kind of trouble?" I liked him; he seemed honest.

"Women. That kind of trouble. Women are easy on Facebook."

I laughed. He looked sheepish, "Of course, not *you*!"

I laughed again. It was the truth. I'd flirted with him, too, and in that moment there was a shadow of Ducu, of the fun, of the playfulness, another bad boy searching for something.

He paid the bill, and I got my own coat. He looked at me funny.

"Forgive me", I said, pulling on the parka. "I'm an American."

"It's interesting to be around!" he said, and we walked to his car.

Before we drove, he put his hands in his lap. The street was very dark and there were no cars. He looked at me, his brown eyes staring into me. He was seductive.

"You know, if you want to write about Ducu, you need to talk to a person who was very close to him."

"Okay."

"You know, Ducu was a Mason?"

"Yes, I know. Like Mozart?"

"Yes, as high up as Mozart, probably. And when Ducu died, we had a ceremony for him in the theater. It was very moving. I will make an introduction." Then he wiped his eyes. "Ducu was a great artist. We have lost so much." He started the car. He drove. He took my hand as we moved through the streets, turning and turning, until he stopped the care where we had started. I missed Ducu like I missed my own free, calm breath. So, I leaned over and kissed the actor, lightly, like a memory. I left the car.

When I returned to the apartment Anya wanted a full report. I said it was fine as I wiped off the makeup.

I got a text from the actor: "You're still here."

I was charmed. I was a grown-ass-mother-fucking-woman who'd had a night out. It was an evening of defiance not to be a scared little girl chasing after a promise of love–no, I'd had a night in the world and for a few hours I felt better, less isolated, in control. But I never got the name of the person the actor thought I should talk with about Ducu, and I never brought up the subject with him again. Anya wanted more information; I gave her nothing.

Waking up the next morning, I was aware that that evening we were going to see Ducu's production of *Coriolanus*. Still in the bed, I watched the cats lying in the sun. I thought of what I wanted to write today. I tried to breathe.

Anya popped her head in, sweet and quiet.

"Hi. How did you sleep?"

"Well, thank you."

"I have some coffee for you."

"Great." I pulled myself from the bed and went over to the couch. She brought me coffee and sat down.

"Would you like to see Ducu's grave?"

I thought for a moment. "Yes, I would. When?"

"We can go to the grave before you leave? Would you like that? We can get in all the traditional things he liked. He believed in honoring the dead. Yes?"

"I'd like that."

We drank our coffee, quietly.

"Why don't we get beautiful today? I can make an appointment for our hair and we can get beautiful for the show–yes?"

"That sounds fun."

Anya went to take a bath. I opened my computer and wrote about conversations Anya and I had had about Ducu's daily meditation that he had put into his schedule the last year of his life. She confirmed for me his interest in Tibet and the trips he'd taken there. I wrote notes. I could focus.

Later that day, we had our hair done. We dressed nicely. Anya wore black. "I'm going to wear black for a year", she said. "I'm going to remember him." Then she held out her left hand. "I did not tell you, but I want to tell you now."

"Yes."

She wiggled her left ring finger and I saw a ring. "We were engaged."

I looked at the small stone. It was tiny. It did not glitter.

Ducu told me once that he was bad at marriage, that he had hurt Maria, that he had hurt me. He had been emphatic that it simply was not his thing. I felt stunned. But time can change a person–death can make you cleave to life.

"He gave this to you?"

"Yes, when I was pregnant."

I looked at her body.

"I tried to keep the baby. He gave me this ring with his whole heart."

"You were pregnant?"

I remembered that I had wanted to have his baby, a very long time ago, but I'd not allowed myself to do it. Perhaps I was just one of many?

"Yes", she said, reaching for my hand with the ring between us, "Yes, but I lost it, just like I lost him."

I believed, in that moment, that I had been just another character in this man's life. I was not a leading role, I was not the friend I thought I'd been. I was a writer, and I needed to remember that, so I wore colors on my body because I was not enough to wear black for him. I pulled my hair up out of my face, off my eyes, ready to see Ducu's last work.

Coriolanus is a story of a general in Rome who fights corruption and fails. Ducu set the play in modern times someplace between Romania and Syria. Sand floating in the air, the production has the feeling of the vastness of a desert. Before the show started, I didn't know what to expect. I saw friends in the hall waiting to enter, there were many people who looked excited to be there, the feeling of the theater very alive. Ducu felt present as the lights faded and went dark, and then…he blew our minds.

Ducu starts the play with the hot breath of a mob. Packs of young people fill the space holding large sticks, ready to strike. They chant in unison, "Facts!" a demand for the truth–the movement and tableaux of the crowd pulled from the local headlines of young people taking to the streets in Bucharest. In Ducu's inverted comedy, the entire stage is dusty with sand, and the mob, the army, the political class, with Coriolanus in the lead, go to war before our eyes, leaving the dead, corruption, and sanity in its wake. A portrait of power and society going mad in its quest for meaning, the production is his last cry for the truth, as well as a testament to the history of Romanian theater, the basis of his life, a search to understand power while also falling apart under its weight. Ducu's*Coriolanus* is not a tragedy but a journey directly into hell: his hell, our hell, culture's hell when our need for power becomes more important than our need to be human.

Politically speaking, Ducu's*Coriolanus* is a meditation on narcissism's place in political campaigns. Ducu was an avid follower of political science and public affairs, and his production has layers of insight that are stunning. The lives of the people are manipulated by corrupt politicians, food is shared onstage and the hungry mob eats and is then left to sleep in the streets, cabals of soldiers move from loyalty to loyalty based on the newest direction of power, the deep bonds of family influence the vision of the general as he jumps ship to help the "enemy" overtake the government that's tricked him out of his power.

Power itself is on trial in Ducu's work–people grow mad with it like a drug and forgo reason and loyalties to maintain it. Each character in the production breaks with reality on some level as they grow or lose power. The mob expands in reach, the manipulators gain control, the leadership moves from being noble to being greedy, and Coriolanus himself, his roots destroyed, finds his mother mad in the desert. The breakdown of family is portrayed as a cancer, a cultural illness that decimates the structure of their world.

Prophetic, Ducu seemed doubtful that neither Romania nor Europe could make it through its deeply embedded fear of change and habitual violence to a more just society. And he was watching a global mass migration happen at the same time he was directing the show. He expressed in interviews and with friends that he was watching in the world exactly what he was directing onstage. Looking at current events through the lens of Shakespeare's timeless language, Ducu had come to his own conclusions about a global culture of greed, mass isolationism, and a trend toward forgetting history. His political insights were married with his creative talent, and his *Coriolanus* had the feeling of CNN live on the scene of a war, as well as of a theater production exploring the depths of a man's disconnection from himself.

Ducu's concern about nationalism is also embedded in the production with the presence of characters who cultishly follow their political leader. They hang on his every dangerous word with the desire to believe him. As nationalism spreads again through Europe and the rest of the world, *Coriolanus* is even more startling as a play to explore. Ducu picked away at nationalism–how can culture go backward into hate so rapidly and with such fervor? Ducu wanted an answer. He masterfully explored the zig-zag of power searching out its place in a shifting world. Moments in his production capture everything with a look, a gesture, and an implication. Ducu was very clear that the global movement toward isolationism was dangerous, that something had not changed in his own country, that the world was growing smaller, igniting like a tinderbox.

It is an unfortunate tradition in the theater that the heads of theaters who die can often become saints, or simply be written out of history. Often, it is through the writing of books by critics, management, and boards that wipes away the memory of an artist who has a rugged past. This sanitizing seems to me to be a kind of survival method to control the life story of an artist and by extension keep your job. In the case of the Bulandra the interim manager, a young woman, stated to the press that now they could "Make Bulandra Great Again", a startling echo of Trump's nationalist call to enact policies in opposition to liberal democracy. Perhaps I'm missing something culturally, that Trump's MAGA (Make America Great Again) is seen as uniquely positive in Romania, yet I am not sure–Ducu was very clear to state at the end of his life that he believed the theater needed to be political again in Romania (and abroad), that it has a role in reflecting the current world and can be a place for civic discourse. I can't imagine him supporting the idea of making Bulandra "great again" when it was making art that was already wowing audiences. In fact, Ducu was very cautious about the commercialization of theater and the "dumbing down" of theater for entertainment's sake–he saw a rise in mindless art in his own culture and around the world.

Coriolanus was Ducu's way of showing how political theater, supported by exciting action onstage, could be a medium that was valuable for our times.

He was looking to jump into the battle of art being a place for dangerous truth–if only he'd had the energy, and the time, to show us this vision more fully.

Ducu may have been a supporter of the royal family of Romania (the Custodian of the Crown, Margareta, was a supporter of the Bulandra and its work in the lab on the top floor of the theater), but he was also a believer that democracy, even flawed, had a place in people's lives, and that freedom of expression and speech was critical for human happiness.

The Bulandra already stands as one of the great theaters of Europe, but it's chilling to think of it promoting insularity when that's the very opposite of what Ducu had hoped for. In his *Coriolanus*, society begins to go mad without a moral anchor, without beauty, without clear truth. The society of the arts can also become lost in the politics swirling around us and we can censor ourselves, hide our genius in exchange for power.

Politics aside, in his *Coriolanus*, I see Ducu in every character, every desperate note, every edgy joke, every call to arms, every loving glance. He is not one character but the play in its entirety–his *Coriolanus* shows the potential for people to deteriorate before our eyes. I loved him more sitting in his theater than I had in thirty years–his vision cut me to the core, his isolation broke me, his brave will to live gave me pride. I was told at intermission that I'd been given his favorite seat and a part of me never wanted to move again–to stay there in his pain, to finally hear his truth that the world is broken, while beautiful.

I wept in the seat.

Anya and Peter came to where I sat after the curtain calls. I was spent. Worn.

"Come on!" Peter berated me. "Pull it together!"

When we left the theater into the night, we could not find a cab so we walked, silent. Sulking, Peter wiped away tears. We found a cab and a restaurant still open for pizza. The food came, so did Peter's guile.

"Sarah, explain to me what that show was about."

"You don't understand it, Peter?"

"No. I just want to hear what you think–if you understood it."

"I don't have to explain anything to you, Peter. I understand the theater, quite well."

"You can't possibly understand what he was trying to say. He was making art about here and you can't understand."

"Shut up, Peter!" Anya said. "That's enough!"

Peter shrugged, hard. "How can she understand? How can you understand, Sarah, you're not from here! And, now he's gone and the truth is all gone."

Leaning in, I said, "Peter, nothing is really gone. You all are well trained artists and you can tell your stories."

"This isn't America!" Peter said. "You have no idea what you just saw!"

Anya called for the check. We all lay money down. We stepped outside and Peter complained about the cold, about the night, about the cab. He refused to step into the cab. Anya yelled at him. He walked into the night and I never saw him again.

"I'm so sorry about that", Anya said in the car. "He's fucked up."

Putting her arm through mine, she took my hand, warmed it like a mother. I had no feelings, just regret, that I'd had to do anything this evening but see Ducu's remarkable production. I had called my father as we rode in the cab and gave him a detailed account of the show. Anya lay her head on my shoulder and listened.

When I hung up with my father, and when we were almost home, she whispered, "I love you my sister. You really care and you really see. I love you."

I felt nauseous. The cold was enough. The war inside Ducu at the end of his life was enough–he put it all on the stage, the conflict, the fury and the mess of life, he'd laid it out in blood before us. So this life, crazy and erratic, was enough. I felt dead.

In the morning, before going to the cemetery, we crossed the street to a florist and bought Christmas flowers and a wreath. We bought candles. I sat on a stool outside in the freezing air. We then got a cab, which weaved through the city. Anya talked about having taken Ducu to doctors appointments–it had been them against the world. I just wanted to see where he rested.

The Bellu Cemetery stands noble in the cold. "Artists Alley" looks like a grittier, smaller version of the Père Lachaise Cemetery in Paris. Busts of ancient people, orthodox crosses, flowers in all forms dot the cemetery. We walked past people crying, we walked past workers fixing up graves–Anya smiled and thanked everyone she saw. "They work very hard and no one appreciates them", she said, offering some candy to a lady cleaning a grave. We arrived at Ducu's plot–he was, she assured me, still there.

Someone had left white roses in a vase. The candles had burned down. The mound of dirt was still high upon him. I knelt and touched the brown earth. I sang the ancient Shema prayer in Hebrew. Anya watched me. She lit a cigarette. I crouched as she walked away.

"Honey?" I asked him, and nothing at all. "Are you okay now? I love your theater, that blue is fabulous…" I grew quiet again when Anya returned.

From out of the background, much as in *Hamlet*, a grave worker approached, asking to speak with Anya. They chatted, Anya returned, laughing.

"She told me that there are many women who come here, cry, put flowers down…some come for hours and talk with him", she said, turning to the grave. "Is that true, baby?" It was a funny moment. And a tad contrived. "That prayer is Hebrew?"

"Yes", I said.

"I've never heard Hebrew before. I felt him say that was finally the right prayer."

I liked the idea that it was the right prayer, but I still had no clear picture of his final days. I had no idea how to write the book. I had a hard time remembering his voice, the past nine days setting me spinning. I was ready to go home.

That night, I got into the bed Ducu had slept in.

I dreamt of fire.

I could not feel the flames.

I was stuck in that theater.

I was looking for him.

Every exit was a false escape.

He was trapped in a curtain, the red material aflame.

He was lost.

I woke in a deep sweat. Quickly dressing, I pulled my bag to the door, ready to leave. Anya put me in a cab, holding my hand through the window, begging me to stay in touch, saying that she loved me, that I was special, that she would never forget me, and that she would come to California soon to visit her cousin in Los Angeles.

"I love you!" she yelled as the car drove away. "I love you! I love you!"

Exhausted, I sank into my seat. The streets leading out of Bucharest toward the airport couldn't have come more quickly. I jumped out of the car, into the airport, sat at a café, and drank coffee.

I counted down time.

On the plane, I thought about the trip. What I'd learned. What I hadn't learned. I tried to weigh it out, find the average of knowledge to bafflement. I couldn't find the balance, so I drank more coffee.

Why hadn't Maria seen me, not at all, not even when I'd asked Anya to reach out to her finally? And, Peter, what was that all about, that fight about Ducu's show? Why so angry at me for disliking his ideas about the world? And, what about the theater–Ducu's theater–what was the real problem? Had I discovered anything? Anything worth writing about?

And how was I going to pay the rent?

ACT 3

"Everything will turn out right,
the world is built on that."

—Mikhail Bulgakov,
The Master and Margarita

San Francisco/New York—Survival, 2019

My apartment–tiny. The ocean–vast.

My cats were happy to see me. Opening my laptop, I wrote to a client, said I was back. I was ready to get to work, and then the jet lag hit me.

Over the past twenty years, I'd paid the bills by being a communications strategist for tech start-ups in Silicon Valley. I also wrote narratives for executives or companies when they were needed to position themselves with the press. I was pretty good at it. Writing the story of a corporation is like writing a play–it's a kind of fiction unto itself. And, since–legally–a corporation is now considered a person, I tried to think of each story as a means to a heart.

Yet I needed to make more money to make up for the trip to Bucharest. Come to think of it, I needed that contract signed with the publisher to finish the book. So, I emailed a friend who had been an agent for writers and asked for a referral to help me with the contract. Promptly, I heard back from him and he'd made an introduction. Within a week, I had a consulting agent who'd help to get the paperwork together. I was starting to think about the business of the book. I was able to focus on that, though the content of my trip still eluded me.

I didn't hear from Anya for weeks. Finally, texting me, she sent a picture of her in Madrid, Spain, where she'd gotten a part on a show for Netflix–a rather famous one where a group of gangsters take over the Spanish Mint and over many seasons robs it. The gangsters fall in love with each other, create havoc, and generally elude the authorities. She said she was friends with the star of that show, that he'd helped her get the role. Sincerely happy her life was moving forward, I sent her my best.

I'd had some time to think about Anya. Appreciating her simple love for Ducu, I realized we had little in common. Away from her, I also wrote a new narrative, something I could be comfortable with, about a young woman in a tough world who'd lost her anchor.

The December holidays were over. I spent January's dim days and black nights writing like mad. My agent drafted the contract, read the book, gave me feedback, and reached out on my behalf to the publisher in Romania.

I received emails from the publisher, as did my agent. I engaged my lawyer who reviewed what the agent had written up. We sent it to Romania. They more than approved: they agreed to the amount and the contract in full. We asked to own the rights, they approved. Delighted they wanted the movie rights, I wrote some more.

My best friend called, asking me to come visit her in New York for a few days in February. Accepting the invitation, I let the publisher in Bucharest know I'd be in New York and asked if I could meet with Adrian, the CEO, who lived in New York. They were delighted, but offered to come to San Francisco first to meet me and my agent to set everything up. So before I left for New York, I arranged to meet with them at Zoetrope, Francis Ford Coppola's restaurant in San Francisco. And I worked some more on the book.

A week before the meeting in San Francisco, the liaison for the publisher emailed me and told me the sad news–Adrian had cancer and could not travel. Receiving treatment in New York, he still wanted to meet me; and so we changed the plans to connect in New York instead.

My consulting agent suggested he and I meet over dinner to discuss things. Picking him up at his house, I discovered he was much older than I'd thought. Around eighty, I guessed. Entering the car, he said, "I'm so lucky to have dinner with such a beautiful woman." We drove to a restaurant and he ordered for us although I'd been about to order for myself. I explained what I hoped for from the book, but he changed the subject and wanted to talk about me–was I single? "Really, you are quite a woman", he said, staring into my eyes.

I had that feeling, the one you only have when you know you are invisible. I could not feel my clothing on me. I could not feel my mind. I was just a thing to him, with, perhaps good fingers to type. And, down at the depth of it all, I knew I just wanted to be taken seriously. But I left it there, just another weird experience with a man–just another moment where you are nothing.

Soon after, I packed my bags again. I bought a ticket to New York. I arranged for the cats to be watched. I'd made enough for rent; and I was ready to get my money from the publishers.

At the San Francisco Airport, people searching for their gates sped past me. Some of them wore masks. Stopping, I glanced at them, wondering why. The virus was in Asia and not in the United States. Some in Italy were ill, yes, but surely it wasn't spreading? Coughing, I walked on.

My best friend lives in Greenwich Village, where I grew up. From my friend's apartment, I saw roofs of the Village. I saw the tip of Christopher Street where Ducu and I had gone to pierce his ears. I saw where my father and I had walked when AIDS ravaged through the streets ransacking lives.

Sitting at my friend's kitchen table, I wrote. I worked on *Ducu Rising*; and I worked on a novel about a journalist who is kidnapped and killed and his mother sells the rights to his life to make a film. It had been bothering me that I'd given up the film rights to *Ducu Rising*. I'd expressed that to my agent, who said it sounded like a good deal and the right time for the story. But I didn't like it–something was not right about my decision to write about Ducu's life, our life, and I still wanted to talk to Maria. I reached out to Anya from New York. I told her of my desire to talk with Maria. She wrote, saying it was impossible, that Maria most certainly would not want to talk to me. But she urged me to keep writing, to finish the book and send it to her. No one could tell the story better than I could, she said, and I should keep to "The True" and complete the book.

Waking up at six-thirty every morning in New York, I'd watch the morning news shows, drink coffee, and write. My agent wrote, saying he'd sent his banking information to the publisher and that he would collect the funds and then pass them on to me. I felt funny about that. I called my father, but he reminded me that many agents do this and that it can work to your benefit. I didn't really know what to do with that, but it was all moving fast and so I decided to trust the agent and wait for the funds.

Days went by. I wrote. I slept. I walked. I went to places I'd been with Ducu to try to jog my memory. I saw friends. Taking in New York, I compared it to Bucharest.

And then it all fell apart.

I received a furious email from the publisher's liaison who said my agent had acted inappropriately: he'd demanded they deposit the money into his account, saying he wanted help buying a house in Romania. Understandably freaked out, they wanted to walk away from the project. They emailed proof. I panicked. Calling my lawyer, I asked him what we should do. The lawyer thought that the agent was the problem and that the deal could be saved if we removed the agent. The lawyer drafted an email firing the agent. I wrote to the publisher and convinced them I'd taken care of the problem. It took a few days until they calmed down. Then they asked me for a bank account where they could send the money. They asked me to sign up with CitiBank because the CEO would send me the funds from New York and it would be more immediate. I went to CitiBank on Sixth Avenue and West Fourth Street. They got me set up with a checking and savings account. They gave me the information to send to the publisher so they could wire me funds. It was going to be fine, the publisher said, let's just keep it calm. "No more drama?" the liaison said.

Back at my friend's house, I checked my bank account. It was low, but it was doable. The funds from the publisher should be there soon. Anxious, I looked out the window at the small world in the large city where I'd grown up.

My parents met in the 1960s when my father was the director of the Judson Poets Theater, which was housed in the massive Judson Memorial Church near Washington Square Park in Greenwich Village. My mother would attend my father's sold out productions of Gertrude Stein plays, original musicals, or mad experiments of the sixties. Cigarette in tow, he was always with an actress. He was slightly round with a Prussian mustache and had hands that always moved.

My mother was a student of theology at Union Theological Seminary uptown, and she came to the theater because her best friend, Al Carmines, Judson's minister, leader of the arts program, and my father's creative partner. Al was still in hiding for being gay, and my mother would be his "beard."

My parents were invited to a dinner. They met. He did not like her. She loved him already. He changed his mind when he saw her eyes, clear and full of intelligence. They left. They made love. They married two months later and spent the next fifty-five years together, and they graciously included me. At their wedding at Judson, artists and activists (complete with signs promoting peace they brought from an anti-war march earlier that morning), family members (aghast at the combination of my parents, the freedom of it, the danger of two religions living together), and musicians filled the church harboring a surprise for my mother at the end of the service: my father had hung lights in the middle of the night to make sure the church was lit well; and then actors sang her favorite songs from his plays.

Theology and theater came together for them, and they liked it that way.

I was born the 18th of August, 1968, the first natural childbirth in our hospital in Brooklyn. The umbilical cord was wrapped around my neck and so my face was blue and taut. Seeing my face, my father had said I looked like a grown woman.

He knew me in a way my mother would not: slightly ahead of myself, slightly more adult than I should be. And this followed me into a life of often finding myself in situations a bit ahead of me, a bit more adult than I could handle. My father treated his precocious child's condition through regular doses of great writing. He'd read to me from authors who faced life with oomph and style: Grace Paley and Shakespeare, James Joyce and James Baldwin. Drawing from his lineage of linguists, he helped me gather some words for the world. Although I was on stage by the time I was six years old, it was the words that thrilled me–it was the sound of the truth in them that I desired.

Attending all of my father's rehearsals, I grew to love the actors as much as I did their words. Very often, a stage manager would "adopt" me, and I would learn how to wait for the light cues or keep the cigarettes away from the leading lady's dress. There was always a young actor or actress who would tell me stories of their day. Dancers found their way into my father's productions, and I would watch them warm their bodies on the floor and then take flight. I would wander backstage to visit the costumes I imagined were my friends. Food was brought into theaters and the world would seem very far away. Lights changed the space, and music made the air thick with sound. I think I was Miranda on Prospero's Island as Shakespeare envisioned for *The Tempest*–my world was filled with sacred monsters and traveling pirates, love and deception. Our world was dreams made into art, where magic and meaning blended. Because my father's theater was in a church, I thought art was its own religion, and the religion I felt in my body was the tradition of my father. I imagined theater was the language of the ancient Torah, the most spiritual strain of Jewish tradition. I felt every play was an ancient language drawn from a deep tradition.

And our country was Brooklyn. I was born and raised in the same two-story brownstone in the heart of an Italian neighborhood. Now chic, Carroll Gardens was once an enclave of misfits at the tip of the borough. We were the first "mixed" family (Protestant and Jewish) in the entire neighborhood, and my father would make respectful eye contact with the mafia boys who guarded the street corners and the local deli. Despising my father's "kind", they seemingly grew kinder after I was born, sometimes "protecting" me from the always present "other" they didn't want on "their" streets.

Old ladies sat at the windows and screamed the names of children to come home to eat. The snow would overtake the streets and we would lie down in the dunes of murky snow. In the summer, the mafia boys would open the nozzles to the fire hydrants and we would run through the water, squealing. Come spring, birds sang in the trees and daffodils grew in the gardens.

Life was filled with parties in my home, artists and radical activists all seated with theologians who got crushes on the actors–my mother cooked for everyone, the kitchen was full, my friends and I made plays and we laughed out loud, parents and children, together.

My father's work was born out of the magical realism tradition. He had no classical training from a drama school but learned the old way as an apprentice, as an assistant and then was made the Living Theater's Managing Director. Julian Beck and Judith Malina were the leaders of the Living Theater, a deeply radical and inventive group that made waves in culture and broke the "fourth wall" (the imaginary wall between the audience and the stage) to explore what Brecht defined as the "epic theater", a place that can help to change the world. After the Living Theater, my father helped to form the Judson Poets Theater, where he helped produce plays by poets like Derek Walcott, and his friend, the writer Maria Irene Fornes. Painters like Robert Rauschenberg and Ed Lazansky made sets. The playwright Harry Koutoukas would arrive in drag and hold my father's hand for good luck. Sometimes the playwright and actor Sam Shepard would show up and he and my father would smoke cigarettes quietly. Inspired by Martha Graham, dancers filled the lower floors and experimented with movement. A wild combination of rock stars, writers, business people, and journalists filled the audience, and the magic of art hummed throughout.

As the decades went by, my father worked in many theaters in the United States, though circled into the second act of his career as a professor at the Yale School of Drama, and in 1981 became the Dean of Theater Arts and Film at the great conservatory at SUNY Purchase, New York. There he selected and taught those who would lead the way for the independent film world as well as actors who would make their mark, like Stanley Tucci, Robert Burke, Seth Gilliam, Edie Falco, Wesley

Snipes, Parker Posey, and others who were later named the "Purchase Mafia."

In 1981, the year my father started at Purchase, the first of many friends died of "gay cancer", the phrase whispered and feared; no one knew to call it AIDS. The news ripped through our lives like wildfire. One friend after another became ill, death started to show its face and my mother, began to make calls to St. Vincent's Hospital in Greenwich Village. The hospital was big and brown and if a person told you they thought they would have to go to St. Vincent's, you immediately began to worry they might die. Every day, another person was admitted for illnesses that made no sense. It seemed like cancer, then a stomach flu, then pneumonia, then their body would start to waste away. And then, looking like a skeleton, they would die, their young body gone, another light burnt out.

In the "outside world", if you had AIDS, you were feared and hated, and people stood outside the hospital with signs saying, "Sinners Die!" They would scream their hatred and you would have to protect yourself to walk through the doors. Fear of an illness became an American obsession. President Reagan didn't speed up research to help end the epidemic, a political movement grew and my mother joined it to create housing for homeless people dying on the streets with AIDS. We went to more funerals than weddings. We lost dear friends who felt like family.

I entered adolescence not believing I would ever survive having a sexual life. I remember my mother manically washing her hands in the kitchen sink and crying at the end of every day. We were in a nightmare.

Ducu knew none of this when we lived and worked in New York. He was simply a theater person in the city and like all theater people, he was afraid of being trapped. As a general rule, we theater people are nomadic, lucky if there is one place to meet for direction in our lives, like a theater or a kitchen. Ducu was aware of this and met people in New York as though finding a long lost brother or sister. The hugs and conversations were long. ("Tell me!" he'd whisper to each new person, "tell me about *you*!") The drinking was part of the welcome dance, the love affair with a new talent in town, the things he knew how to navigate.

Our apartment was around the corner from the Chelsea Hotel. From our bed, we could look out at the gardens amidst the tall city buildings. We would listen to a lone musician play his horn, while plastic bags and birds clung to the trees. The combination of beauty and scruffy dirt made our lives fall in line with a grand tradition of artists on the fringe. I would tell Ducu about all the people who'd lived in the Chelsea Hotel, the poets and painters and punk stars who'd died there. I told him about the love affair between Patti Smith and Sam Shepard, how they'd hidden in their hotel room and created the play "Cowboy Mouth."

"Yes, yes, I know that play", he'd whispered in the dark.

"And, so you know about the crow?" I'd said. "How they are in a world of their own?"

"You can stay in a world of your own for only so long." He kissed my ear.

"Yes, but they made something."

"Memory is also something." He kissed me harder.

I didn't know how to put words to my fear, that I was, like Patti, a beloved part of the life of an artist while he was married. Sam had been married, too. The difficult truth is that I came from a tradition where men felt they had to reject the confines of society and very often left their wives for an illusory freedom. I didn't know how to explain how I'd been raised to be a muse and also a mistress. It was not a conscious thing, no one had meant to hurt me, but really, a woman had little power in our world unless she rejected everything and accepted a starring role as a man's muse. As the protectors of a man's "freedom", women were meant to be wild with our own freedom, our own sex, our own ability not to "hold him down"–our lover, our man trying to find *his* fragile truth. In my world, the women who inspired me had a special status, we were the ones allowed to break the rules of marriage to ensure the man could keep creating, and if proving ourselves loyal, perhaps we might have our own freedom and voice in the game. And so I was meant to be grateful, to maintain the energy from my body to drive his ability to make his body of work at the expense of my own.

"Do you know Patti Smith?" I'd asked him.

"Yes, of course! 'Jesus died for somebody's sins but not mine.' Wow, she wrote that, yes?" He'd whispered her lyric like a prayer.

I'd had no words then for what I wanted to say. Perhaps we were like one of Smith's lyrics–driving, poetic, and fading out to a steady beat. The sounds of Smith circled around me as the sounds of the Chelsea Hotel hummed on through the night and Ducu lay on his right side looking out the window. We had been silent, believing we were a part of our own history, a part of the history of the city: alone in our reality, for just a little while.

Yet no one could have prepared us for the breath of fresh air and fun that Ducu was. Eating, he took complete pleasure, sucking the bone–the very last of the juice licked from his fingers. He had a joke for every occasion and convinced us that our Jewish jokes were really Romanian jokes that, he stated with a grin, "You are lucky to have!" He would sleep until eleven a.m., and with rituals only he could understand he'd transform the shower into a place where he communed with God. To relax, he would watch films and listen to music. And he would never rush his movements, since moving too fast, he believed, could throw off your system. At parties, he would find the most beautiful women and the most interesting children and men who knew how to laugh. Walking down the street, he had a stride of music about him, his long legs thrusting forward and his slightly hunched back weaving side to side. He and I would lie on our couch in our apartment on our noisy street in Manhattan and talk for hours, him sharing stories of his past, me my hopes for what was to come, him making me laugh, the pillows falling to the floor, his laughter flying over the tops of our heads. He would break hearts with stories of his country, the place he returned to at night when dreams took him home to the curtains of theaters and the smell of his son's hair.

His desperate love for his country didn't stop him from taking me to Christopher Street in Greenwich Village and getting his ear pierced. I don't remember the reason why he wanted to have the procedure done, but I do remember the air as it stood still, me watching like a witness, his eyes closed, tears close to his lids. I loved that he wanted to express himself, adorn himself with art and play a bit with his fashion, which was emerging before me in layers of black and bright colors. Later, he allowed me to clean the piercing with alcohol, his head in my lap, his eyes looking up into the ceiling. Over time, he would pierce his ears only in places that made him happy; the piercings climbed up his ears, giving him an original, wild look.

Yet Ducu's adventures in New York were fraught with conflict: the grocery stores had too much food and he would cry thinking of those at home who had too little, the restaurants offered too much pasta on a plate and he would send it back to share with the cooks, the dogs on the streets looked so very familiar and he would wonder what language they spoke, the cats had too much longing in their eyes, the weddings lacked the right amount of champagne and music, the holidays were light on traditions. We Americans, we did not appreciate our freedom, our money. We were lacking in poetry, lacking in awe.

And, most dangerously, he said we didn't have humor to rely on, we didn't get the joke, that the joke was on us, that we were but players in the world. He knew something we did not, that joy was something to be weighed and shared with people because, soon, he knew, the pain would come.

The pain did come to us when we went to see one of the first productions of Cirque du Soleil in their first million dollar tent. The circus rolled into town and my father bought us tickets to see the performance. Cirque du Soleil was life-changing as art, as well as a game changer as commerce. After the circus ended, the hall was filled with screams and feet stomping. Ducu then turned to us and said, prophetically, "We're fucked." He said that now everything was to be a huge spectacle and we would have to keep up. He questioned if America could keep up with this wave of change coming from Canada. Could we be as big, grand, and rare? We didn't have the answers for him that night.

Later, we saw Martin Scorcese's film *Goodfellas*, about the life of the mob. This movie also seemed epic and grand; though the shots were tight on violence and sex, Scorcese continued to amaze with his pacing and grand hand at storytelling.

Ducu had a response to that film as well. With a hand on his head, he moaned, "Oh, fuck me! Everything must be deeper and bigger on stage to make any audience believe anything now." Lighting a cigarette, he thought hard about keeping up with the times, though I believed he could do it–make theater that could enthrall us, take us in, capture us off guard.

At that time, the windows of Barney's department store were all the rage. A few blocks from our apartment in Chelsea, Barney's windows were the Internet of the time. The images were political in nature, or stunningly chic. We'd all line up to see what the store was saying about the times. We would finish dinner and then walk south to peer into the windows. We'd look at color, and Ducu would talk about the shape of the clothing, the cut, the experience of being in the presence of such beauty.

Ducu would leave in the early part of the day to go to rehearsal. He was directing "Cabal of the Hypocrites" by Mikhail Bulgakov, a play about Molière but really a play about corruption in the theater and the world. He might return late and always wanted to talk about what he was doing. He was practical, thinking through the steps of the play, thinking through the interconnections in the scenes. His was a mind like a steel trap, and sometimes he wanted to walk a bit to get the day sorted. If he went alone, I'd imagine him alert, telling the story of the play in his mind, walking quickly and not brooding, but fretting over his next step. He rarely was over-confident, instead filled with a need to tell a story, something intimate and personal for him translated into something grand and big. Grand and big, that was Ducu and that was New York–they matched each other and hummed in unison.

New York was a massive love affair for him. He wanted a life there, yet he didn't know how to get it. Regardless, he knew the subway routes into Brooklyn where he would sit for long hours with friends and talk about the theater. He read the books from bookcases and told stories into the evening. At Passover, he cried over the familiarity of the food. He looked out onto the Brooklyn streets, the trees large and the light from the houses dim. I watched him look at the world around him, saw an inner conversation I could not understand–he was taking it all in while simultaneously battling with his loyalty to Romania, to his theater and his family. He sat alone on the stoop of my parents' house in Brooklyn and lit his cigarette, his breath cold, the smoke unclear.

In early 1990s, the world was breaking open like a vibrant, clean egg, and we thought there could be a way to make a new life for everyone in our lives: wives, children, parents, artists, if only we just stayed the course, stayed strong as we made connections in a brave new world. But outside the windows of that New York, I watched as Ducu began to suffer a unique guilt, a Romanian ache that drew him into a lifelong conflict with a past he found he could not change.

And in truth, I saw rising Europe as the place to be in the world and I had no idea how to be a part of it. America was a "superpower" yet it was crawling along a moral battlefield with conservative beliefs judging my world of the theater and sexuality. We were tempting wars abroad and the arts were suffering from the loss to AIDS. My best friend was working for the European Union and she would call me with the thrill of a unified Europe. I was hearing excitement from her while Ducu was being called to visit theaters throughout Europe. I was in the wrong culture and wrong country for what I wanted: a country of theater, of magic and the promise of Europe. I watched from far away with longing. And, more difficult yet was that I grew up in a time when the theater was dying, particularly the most experimental and exciting of our theater world.

The death of Charles Ludlam in 1987 of AIDS was one of the hardest blows to bear for my family.

The founder of the Ridiculous Theatrical Company located at 1 Sheridan Square in the Village, Charles was revered for his classical plays filled with the same "wink and nod" approach one might have found in Communist theater. His was a theater of the absurd, high camp and cross-dressing but it was grounded in Vaudeville, burlesque, opera, science fiction, and film. Dressed to the nines as Camille, Charles had played a woman with a full chest of hair, and famously quoted the actual lines to subvert the now ugly use of words, "Throw another faggot on the fire" to ironic roars of laughter and the rolling of his eyes. Charles also made the curtain call a work of art, he would flirt with you from the corner of the stage, seem to drag his skirts center stage, take the slowest and most luxurious curtsy, then he would have trouble getting up, then he would be victorious as he stood baiting you on for more applause.

The small theater would shake with joy that a person could so defiantly take in the love of an audience, knowing full well that most culture hated what he stood for: love, sex, and being courageously different from others. Each member of the company, including Black-Eyed Susan, Lola Pashalinski, and Ethyl Eichelberger, could draw out a curtain call to the cat-calls and screams of the audience. I loved those curtain calls as a child as much as I enjoyed the plays, yet it was in their bows where I learned about the defiance of the actor, and the demand to be acknowledged. So, when Charles died, our community shrunk in heart, the curtain calls were never the same, the light of life was dimmed. My father directed the memorial service for Charles and we all stood on stage at the end and wept. For years, his partner Everett Quinton valiantly kept the theater going, only to have it close, the cost of making theater too enormous.

Ducu saw a production at the Ridiculous when he was in New York in the 1990s. He had walked with us down the steep stairs into the theater, what used to be the Café Society where Billie Holliday had performed. Sitting in his seat, he roared with laughter, wiped his eyes from the sheer audacity of the show. Sitting there he howled and then he sat forward and stated that *this* was what theater can be–true, raw, funny, and deeply connected to the outsider's experience in culture. He never saw Charles perform, but we told him about Charles and told him that now it was all "different." Ducu had nodded his head in understanding. He smiled sweetly at us. I remember that he ordered a drink and toasted to Charles's memory in the small restaurant above the theater. My mother had been holding Everett's hand. My father was sitting with the playwright Maria Irene Fornes and my godfather, the dramaturg Leon Katz. Ducu and I had been sitting with the camp poet and my hero, Harry Koutoukas, who held my hand and watched my lover with great interest. Ducu had made the toast, his accent now slightly that of New York. All had raised their glasses and in that moment it was as whole a picture of my childhood and my life that I could give him.

But, Charles was gone. Many said he'd been the genius we needed, and any genius we had was now lost. His absence was so visceral it left a hole in the air.

"It's sad you've lost him", Ducu said to me that night at the Ridiculous as he sipped his drink. "He told the truth through being funny. That's very hard to do."

"Yes. I'm surprised you liked it", I said to him.

"Why? You think I can't understand what it's like to have to 'dress up' and cause a scene because people hate you?"

"No! Of course you can understand it."

"I understand this humor! I understand it better than you know." His face was red. "Baby, you know when we first met, you know what an actor told me at the Royal Court Theater?" He lit a cigarette. He inhaled, and his eyes bulged. "The actor was black.

British black, but he told me the truth. Want to know what he said?"

"Yes", I said.

"He said that no matter what I did, the British, fuck me, all of Europe will probably always see me as the 'Nigger from the East.' That's what they think of us, Romanians, we're like the leftover cattle from a time of invasion. So I understand this humor because it's my humor, it's my reality as well. Not much separates me from Charles. We are different. We can't be conquered." His eyes had been fierce and cold with fact.

The gaping void left by Charles and so many artists who had died of AIDS placed another layer of distance between us. I couldn't provide a world in New York that would be a new world for him, and he could see our glaring loss with clarity. The loss to the theater was so enormous, so weighty I came to understand I was part of something dead. And in 1992, only two years into our relationship, I could see that Ducu needed to continue to fight to be alive. Yet together we were surrounded by ghosts from our pasts, those cut down by AIDS, those cut down from Communism. Everywhere, ghosts were everywhere.

And then he began to drink more. Friends let me know they were concerned about the booze, but

I was too afraid to see it. He started to have nightmares. He missed home. He wept.

Not too long after Ducu left America for the last time, I sent him an amulet for his neck.

I got a call from him, late in the night, his words slurring, "I got your present. But I threw it out the window. We kept getting lost in the car and I think you put a spell on it. You put a spell on it just like you put one on me. I threw it out the window. I watched it go away." I could not speak, he kept slurring. "I watched *you* go away." Soon afterwards, I got calls in the middle of my night. Always slurring, he was so hard to understand. He always left the same message on the machine, "Where *are* you? Where *are* you?"

I did not know what to do. Something deep and solid was between us; the distance, the catapulting of his career, the reality of responsibilities, my own desire to find myself in the world. We broke.

Destroyed, I flew to California. We had no Internet then. He could not find me. I could not find him.

We didn't speak for twenty-five years.

Time crawled, change came.

It was a desert without him.

I remembered all of this looking out of my friend's apartment window. There were ghosts in the streets of the Village. There were ghosts in all of the theaters. I remembered all the loss. I remembered the dead, and now, Ducu was one of them–floating out in the streets looking for a new production to create. I looked over the rooftops and my eyes landed on Lower Manhattan, it too was changed, 9/11 had restructured the bones of New York; it was rebuilt, slick and perhaps no longer my home. I couldn't admit it to myself, but I had been lost for some time, a scattered person searching for the life that died, and a theater world that had died with it.

Perhaps I didn't belong anywhere.

I reached out to a dear friend Romanian, a theater designer and old friend of Ducu's, who lived in New York City. I'd not seen her in twenty years and it was lovely to connect. She invited me up to her house near Columbia University, and so I jumped on the subway for the long ride up. I had only travelled a few stops when I had a deep urge to reach out to Lars. This always happened to me, when I gave myself a moment to stop I would think of him–his hands, his eyes, how he listened. I called to wish him happy birthday as the train raced uptown. I explained to him where I was. I explained to him what I was writing. I paused, took a deep breath and told him Ducu had died. There was silence, I heard him collect his thoughts, "When you get home, call me. I'll bring you something and we can make dinner. Okay?" I was frightened by how excited I was to see him, to feel his attention, so, I said yes, but turned off my heart and continued heading uptown.

I sat in the living room of my friend, Olivia the designer, whose sense of style was still perfect. She served me tea. She offered chocolate. I tried to tell her about the trip to Bucharest, about the strange experience I'd had, and about the book. "Let me read it!" Olivia insisted, and so, later that night when I got back to my friend's house I sent her the first draft of the book. I wrote some more waiting for my friend to arrive back from Europe. A few hours before midnight, my best friend arrived home full of news from her travels.

"And then!" she said, opening a bottle of water with verve, "I got the *last* seat on the plane, because that was it–that was the last flight to the states because of the virus."

"Don't you have to quarantine or something?"

"I guess."

She'd shrugged. So had I. The news said it was possible the virus was already in the States, but no one could get Trump to say one way or the other what was going on. I'd lived through the AIDS virus and that virus was easy to see. People faded right in front of you, wasted away. This virus was hard to see; they said it hit you in the chest and then you needed to be on a ventilator for weeks at a time. I watched New York's Governor Cuomo's daily reviews of the virus, and he scared the shit out of me, and I started to wonder if I would get stuck in New York.

I emailed the liaison to the publisher in Bucharest and told him I was concerned about the virus. He said Adrian was too sick to see me, and that we should arrange something else. I said okay, and then I went home to California. Distracted by Governor Cuomo's reports, I failed to notice my bank account hadn't been filled with the publishers' money.

It became March, and California, like much of the United States, shut down due to COVID-19. I received the news that Adrian was very ill, and that due to COVID, MediaPro had to stop work immediately to safeguard against illness. The streets of San Francisco were empty, and overnight it was a ghost town. The world went indoors and I was afraid.

Lars started to leave care packages at my door. He never knocked, just left something sweet and kind. I accepted each gift aware that my stomach was fluttering with each package. He did not give up. He did not go away. He stayed focused on making sure there was food in the house, masks to wear, cleaning solution–all the things I didn't have because the money hadn't arrived from the publisher. I finally invited him in when I heard a package being placed against the door–he came for dinner and I decided I was a fool. This was a man who really saw me, loved me–was very much alive. What was I waiting for?

Days became weeks, and weeks became months. I stayed inside. I watched the news. Every day, it seemed Trump made up new ideas and new policies, and none of them helped the country. During the daily press conference regarding COVID there would be a bit of time for health information, but then Trump would take the microphone and fight with the press. We all started to watch these news conferences with mouths open. It was a train wreck and Trump's lies spread across the world. The COVID rates grew. I feared for my parents who were now stuck in their assisted-living home. No money came. No money came for anyone. Everything was shut down.

I asked Anya for help. What did she recommend regarding the funds from the publisher? She told me everything was shut down there as well. All productions had been closed, everyone was locked inside.

I realized I had to wait it out. I had to survive with Lars coming to visit, and even though we all found a way to live, we were also finding a way to love.

The simple things became more important. The light off the sea became the background for the day. The cats roaming back and forth between rooms had their own story. Morning was long, and drifted into day. Night was a relief.

I took *Ducu Rising* and turned it into a screenplay. I had nothing else to do, and nowhere to go with the book itself. I didn't really like the book–I was still uncomfortable exposing so much of my privacy, and so I turned the screenplay into a deeper look at Ducu's experience living under totalitarianism. I sent it to Anya to see what she thought. I also sent it to Olivia in New York. Olivia called me and told me she loved it. She had marvelous feedback: I should go deeper into the pain of his experience, try to flesh out his youth. Olivia touched me deeply with her ideas, and then she said, "You have talent. Stay with it." The long days inside the apartment had left me with a feeling that, if anything, I could write down what I saw inside myself and that perhaps this could help me survive.

I spent weeks in the screenplay with Ducu's memory. I tried to imagine his childhood. I tried to imagine when he first started to drink. I tried to imagine how he and Maria had made a life in the hot glare of corruption, then, and even today. I rebuilt his life in my mind and started to imagine who could play him. Javier Bardem was the only person who came to mind, and so I kept writing with Bardem's piercing eye, his textured hands, alive in my mind.

Anya wrote me back, concerned about me. Had the money arrived from the publishers? If not, she asked me to send her an email with the contract and she would personally go to them to help. She also told me that she'd made a great connection with Jose, the director of the show for Netflix, that because of COVID she was unable to leave Romania, but they wanted her to have a creative partnership with their company. She'd signed a contract to do a documentary in the Middle East to explore artists living there and how they kept going during COVID. It was an interesting topic, and she stated she had received an advance.

"Would you like to work on it with me?" she asked, quietly.

"Sure, but in what way?"

"We can research and perhaps you can write it?"

"But, it's your experience, Anya. You need to go and find it yourself."

"But you have a good way of capturing what is important. We can have a project and I can get you some money."

I needed the money. I needed something to do. I liked the topic. I agreed.

I waited for her response to the screenplay for *Ducu Rising*. Waiting, I talked to a dear friend, an actress who had worked with Ducu. I told her about the screenplay and she asked to read it. She loved it and suggested that we do a read through of it on Zoom with another actor who was an old friend. We arranged to read it, signed up our friend to read Ducu's part. I invited Anya and asked her to read one of the roles, but she declined, saying she was too emotional about it, she wanted to listen. My friend, the actress, thought it was going to be hard for me to listen and take notes if I were to read one of the characters, so I pleaded with Anya to read a role, and she said she would try.

When we met on Zoom, the two American actors read the roles beautifully. When it was time for Anya to read, she declined, and instead wept through the entire reading. Her face made strange shapes on Zoom, she could barely breathe. My friends ignored her and kept going–when it was finished the two actors gave me notes, that in general they liked the script a lot. Anya dried her eyes. She blew her nose. Gazing at me from the screen, she said, "I love it so much. You have told the True. I think we should send it to Jose and see if Netflix might like it."

"You think Jose would like it?"

"Why not? It's about a European director–he is one as well, he grew up in the theater, I think he will understand."

"He grew up in the theater?" I asked, plaintively.

"Yes, like you and Ducu. His father was a designer. His mother was wild. He's one of us. He will understand. Send it to me!"

I pictured Jose in a theater. I saw him in a chair looking at the lights in the ceiling. I thought, perhaps, he smoked, secretly. So, I agreed and sent the clean PDF of *Ducu Rising*, the screenplay, directly to Anya to send to Jose in Spain.

Weeks passed. June arrived. I finally received an email from Jose's private email account. He warmly stated that they loved the script and wanted to make an offer but we should meet on Zoom first. We arranged for a Zoom. I sent him emails. He responded with the news that they were still shooting, and were preparing the final season of their show to air on Netflix. He told me that they were still working in Spain, though he understood all films and television had been shut down in the United States. This was all true, Europe was bearing the weight of shooting while Hollywood was closed. Jose was warm, his English was poor–he apologized profusely–and he always signed off "with respect".

I wondered what Jose was like, so I did a search for him. He could be found speaking in short promotional videos for his show, though I found a documentary about the making, and phenomenon, of his show on Netflix. He had small shoulders, alert and passionate eyes, small hands and a wide smile. He spoke only Spanish during the film, although the actors moved in and out of English. There was a scene that struck me, during an outside shoot rain had fallen hard and seemed to ruin their plans. Yet Jose pressed on, asking the most of the team, raising his voice while touching a person's shoulder–he was badgering them with love and I found this compelling. He seemed to get right into the scenes with the actors, and this reminded me of Ducu, of the European tradition of the director as part of the action. I felt I knew him.

I heard back from the publishers' liaison that MediaPro had been sold in a private sale due to the CEO's health. I was informed that his daughter was taking over, would oversee my book, and that I should wait for more information. I secretly longed that the book would not be published. The more I read the screenplay, the more I felt it was somehow more true, more interesting, and I was also nervous still that I was being manipulated to write something sensational about Ducu.

During this period of seclusion, I wrote and wrote. I kept waking up early and refined the screenplay. I worked with my friend on another screenplay about the journalist whose mother sells the rights to his story. I outlined other ideas. And, I worked. I also interviewed Anya to help her with her documentary. I was happy to keep things professional with her. She was, to say the least, exhausting.

(*Exhausting.*)

I offered her a name for her documentary: "Finding Home". She'd told me she was always trying to find her home, that she'd lived in Istanbul for a few years and loved it. That she was connected to the Middle East and had spent time there as well. That she wanted to interview actors there to understand their world. I asked if she wanted to shoot her experience as an orphan looking for home? She liked the idea and so I wrote some ideas for her. She sent them to Jose, and she soon wrote me back that although what I had written was good they wanted her to figure it out for herself, that she needed to write her own story–I totally agreed. Yes, she wanted to pay me for what I had done, for the help thinking it through, so, she said, she'd wired me some money.

I thought more and more about *Finding Home*. It had its claws in me and I did not know why. I woke one morning in a sweat–what exactly was the documentary about? In the dim morning, I had a flash that it might make no sense to have this idea fully funded; it was just a wisp of a concept, and it all lay on the shoulders of Anya to be compelling enough to produce a story that would make audiences care. Yet why should they care about a person who was from one country with an old regime to an even older country with a newer, more violent war? The doubt had struck me hard. I felt unclear, and yet who was I to doubt this–that a woman from Eastern Europe might not tell a wonderful story about death in the Middle East? Shaking my head, I was happy for the income and happy she was trying her hand at new things–I mean, Ducu must have seen the talent in her, right?

Weeks went by, and the publishers also contacted me; they wanted to set up a time to talk with the new owner. More weeks went by, and we could never set up the meeting. Finally, Anya said I should just ask them for an answer either way whether they wanted to move ahead. Their answer? No. No, it was no longer a property they wanted, but they would pay me for my work. No, they were focused on salvaging their television production and a book was not in the business plan. I was relieved.

(*I was relieved. God, I was so relieved. Privately, I knew that my story would hurt Maria and Anton. I was so relieved I left the manuscript in the computer like an orphan. Though I could see Anya everywhere. She was a shadow, moving along the walls of my life.)*

Jose contacted me from Spain and said they were backed up as well, that we would connect in August and move ahead with the contract prior to the meeting. Jose wrote me with the offer and it was excellent and in line with industry standards. I sent it on to my lawyer, he agreed. I asked Jose what he wanted and he said I could send my requests for the contract to him to expedite the process, so we did. Jose approved, added his own language about me being on set and part of the team, and that they wanted to turn it into a limited series of six episodes to be shot in the new year for release in 2021. I was excited, happy that the book could sleep a while until I was sure it was ready, and then I told my parents. They were thrilled that something positive had come from the sadness of Ducu's death.

(Where was Ducu now? I thought. Where was his soul? Where was his memory? Where had he gone?)

I asked Anya if she wanted to play herself in the series. She told me, no, Jose had thought it best she focus on being a producer, that she had talent and liked to solve problems. That seemed right to me. Yes, she loved to chase a problem.

"I think you should be very proud of the screenplay", she said.

"Why?"

"Because it really sounds like you. The book is good, but it's a bit stiff."

I had to agree. The book was tight, loaded like a gun, but for me, it had little force.

"Well, I think not being able to talk to people made it less interesting." I said, sheepishly.

"I agree. But you have a strong voice. You should let it flow more, you should trust yourself–I feel sometimes you hold back."

Yes, perhaps she was right. Secluded, I was sitting with no distractions–there were only the stories, there was only time.

Anya started texting me in the early morning. The sound would wake me, and I began to feel them arrive even before they pinged. I would awaken at six thirty in the morning prior to her text. I'd make coffee and wait. Then, she'd send a note of encouragement, or ideas. It became a pattern of my morning. They became, her notes, a part of my life.

Months of COVID passed. Months of worry passed. I was able to apply for COVID relief for money and also for a cut on the rent. As with millions of others, my consulting dried up and we spent the days watching the news of more death, more ruin. I was addicted to the news.

Then, a story came to me. And, then, the actresses I saw in the role came to me. I wrote a screenplay called *Mixed Messages*, and I wrote it for Diana Ross and her daughter, Tracee Ellis Ross. The story is that of a great American opera singer (Tracee) who goes on a TV show to explore her roots. Her DNA is taken and she finds out that she is Jewish, leading her to learn from her mother, a retired social worker (Diana) that her mother had had a love affair with a Jewish guy from the civil rights movement–

and that he was her father. Yet what transpires in this dystopian story is how her public surprise (that she is Jewish) coincides with an anti-Semitic takeover of the country, and the singer is left to find a way to fight against the war, with art.

I wrote and wrote. It was my voice, and my country. I thought, well, could I really write this and not be black? The streets had been full of our country marching to say that Black Lives Matter–who was I to write this story? Then I began to think about Tracee Ellis Ross, how she was black and her father was Jewish. So, I wrote and wrote trying to speak to the Jewish in her, and I wrote the mother's role to reflect the hardships of the civil rights movement of the 1960s. I finished the script. I liked it. I sent it to my father and to Olivia for their feedback. Both my father and Olivia thought it was super and that I was on to something good, but both said I should go further, make it more dangerous. So, I worked on it for a few more weeks, until it felt done.

One morning, I wrote to Jose, saying I had another script, that I would love his feedback–just to see if he had ideas or if he felt it was good. He urged me to send it. I did, and the next day he wrote me, "I read this in one reading! It's amazing. I want it!"

I was starting to think I might be lucky. Who could be this secluded and actually work? I had read that Hollywood–more specifically the streaming networks like Netflix–were alive and well buying the rights for movies and series. It was a "gold rush" to fill the waves with projects to meet the needs of all of us stuck at home, watching television.

So, I wrote some more. This time, I wrote a screenplay and named it *Waves*. I wrote it with Jose in mind because I'd watched all of his work to get a feel for him. The story I wrote was also inspired by his leading lady who played a pregnant cop on his series for Netflix. She was wild and interesting. And I thought a story for a woman my age that was about rebellion could be fun for viewers. Inspired by Lars who used to race sailboats on San Francisco Bay, I wrote a story about the worlds' fastest Catamaran sailboat, and the crazy Silicon Valley titan who owned the boat. The crew, led by a woman, decides to mutiny against the owner, which compels them to make a Faustian bargain that must be reconciled with rebellion. I liked this script as well, and after sharing it with Lars, I sent it to Jose. He loved it, and some months later, he bought it.

The story of the sea was a return to myself. I had the time, so I took the time to listen to the ocean outside my window. I did not hear the texts or emails coming at me, I only heard the nature of water outside the window. I wrote and wrote a "bad guy"–the owner of the racing boat–and I made him a composite of all the greedy assholes I had met or worked for in Silicon Valley. Yet I made the real enemy the obsession with technology–the longing for perfection found in tech, the disconnection from humanity, from our humanness. I wrote passionately, blindly, and made small edits to the script and wondered, quietly, why Jose had bought this piece without giving me notes for what could be improved. Trying to edit it on my own, I longed for a conversation with him. I'd been working for some months with a film director who lived and worked in Los Angeles–he'd demanded a lot of me, he'd wanted meetings and calls. He'd been the one to say, "Go deeper" on that script. When I mentioned this to Anya, that it was odd Jose had no notes, she scoffed and said, simply, "You think all directors are the same?"

Then, as though knowing my feelings, Jose wrote to me, a lovely letter, that his aunt in New York, a producer, was encouraging him to move to New York. He told me, confidentially, that he was not happy in his company, and that he was thinking of leaving. Would I be interested in working with him, and could he purchase *Mixed Messages* and *Waves* for his use? I saw no reason not to–he assured me that he had a great relationship with Netflix and was confident he could make the transition. Then, he asked if he could send *Mixed Messages* to Diana Ross because his aunt was a dear friend of hers. I agreed, of course!

Time passed. We were stuck inside.

I had not felt sad about Ducu for a long time. I liked that Anya was moving on. I liked that I was working, and loving Lars, so I pressed on–I just carried a private torch for my life, with the hope we would all be free soon, free to vote out Trump, free to have a vaccine, free to breathe the air outside our homes.

And then Anya told me she was pregnant.

She'd started to have an affair with a doctor in Bucharest, a man who had some power. She said she was in love. She said he'd helped Ducu when he was sick. She told me, quietly, that she was pregnant with twins and planned to have the babies.

I was viscerally turned off by this news. She was so clear about having the babies and having the doctor take care of it, of them, my stomach turned at the thought that she was going to use this man for her needs. I was so turned off I called my best friend. Turning on Zoom, she looked at me, saying, "What's upsetting you? Some women are like this."

"I know. But, I have a bad feeling…maybe I don't know her."

"But, you do. Right? You know her?"

"But, perhaps…"

"She used Ducu?"

"Yeah."

"How can you find out?"

I had no idea. I didn't have the connections I thought I had in Romania. I'd been shut out and had not heard from any of the friends I'd made when Ducu was alive.

"I just have a feeling."

"Trust it", my best friend said.

So, I didn't.

A few days later, Anya called, saying she'd miscarried. I was sad for her, but relieved she was no longer using this man.

"Are you sad?" I said.

"Yes. No. I probably should not settle down, I need to love myself first."

That sounded spot-on. And, truth be told, I needed to love myself more, so I cut her some slack.

I got back to the emails coming at me from the Romanian publishers and from Jose, who was trying to find a way to get me money: the banks in Europe, I was told, were backed up and crazy due to COVID.

Summer passed with protests and riots in my country. We watched, glued to the news, the images of black men being killed by white police officers. The protests grew and grew. I became afraid to go outside, not because of safety, but the isolation was getting to me. Lars would have to coax me out of the apartment, take my hand and walk me by the ocean. I held his hand tightly, it was getting to me, being separate from the world was shifting my view of my life. I felt small, lost in the dark.

Jose wrote me that his mother had died of COVID. We sent notes of affection and care back and forth. He was distracted but still working. He and I started to email about our vision for work, our favorite movies and directors. We shared ideas for a future of making work. I tried to imagine his cadence. I tried to imagine his eyes. I don't know why I didn't insist on a phone call. I don't know why I thought it was enough.

I worried about my parents. I talked to them on FaceTime. We pushed through the summer and into fall where the presidential election was starting to heat up. The sense of fear that Trump could win again began to flow between me, my friends, my family–everywhere, the anxiety of his possible re-election became more prevalent. On the news, the anchors and guests were openly calling Trump a fascist–it was undeniable, the locking up of immigrant children in cages and separated from their families, the calls for violence against people of color, the anti-semitic statements flowing from the "Proud Boys"–all of it oozed through our lives, filled our dreams, distracted us from life.

In October, Jose returned to me with remarkable news: Diana Ross loved the script and wanted to do it. She'd passed it on to her daughter, who also wanted to do it and co-produce it as well and bring it to Disney with whom she had a contract. It was the only good news, it was the only hope, it was that light I'd needed.

Yet, Jose warned me, "She wants you to add almost fifty more pages–make it longer, make it more full."

I agreed. Diana needed more, she was a national treasure; and I needed to write something wonderful.

I asked Jose if we should bring in another writer, a black writer to make sure we had the right voice. "Why?" he had replied. "You are a writer, just focus on the story." I paused, I had wanted to extend the project to include Joie Lee (sister of Spike Lee, who was a wonderful actress and writer on her own), whom I'd grown up with in Brooklyn–I thought she would add so much to the project. Had I made a mistake? Why was Jose interested in this story, this very one, now? Why wouldn't he want to make it better? I felt, like a quick swift punch in the ribs, that I'd not waited long enough with this script–that I should have extended it to American artists–but then, who was I? Anya made sure to remind me of this: "Jose is giving you a great opportunity. You should listen to him." But the more I sat with it, the more I felt I was not protecting the core of the project, so I emailed Jose again insisting we should bring in another writer. He never responded. I felt I was losing my own country, the story of our conflict, and that that was something Jose had little interest in. So, why, again, why did he want to make *Mixed Messages*?

I asked Anya this question, and she replied, "Because he's Jewish."

"What?"

"Yes, but this is Spain, they hide being Jewish, they all do. He's Jewish, and he cares about this story. You know, his aunt in New York is Jewish, and that's one of the reasons she wants him to move–so he does not have to lie."

"What is the lie, exactly?"

"You have to remember, in Europe, being Jewish is still–complicated. I mean, look at you, you are so kind to me, and I could not understand why.

Then I told my mother you were Jewish, and she said that is why, Jews are generous when you are in their family. You Jews have a good system, you know how to survive, you build families that last. And, that's what it is, I consider you family now. So does Jose. You see, it all makes sense."

I looked around my apartment. I saw books I'd been given about being Jewish. This idea, this cliché she'd just shared, that we are somehow different–our own race–was documented in many of those books. I took a deep breath, "It's true that Jews have to hide. So that's why he wants to do this film, and this film first?"

I heard Anya sigh. "No, he thinks that Diana Ross is a big deal and will get lots of awards for this role. You know, I don't really understand it myself, I don't totally feel this script, I think it needs more. But he thinks it's enough to start and you can fix it and it will get a lot of attention."

Somehow, that felt right–he was drawn into this for the talent, and she, well, it didn't matter if Anya "felt" the script, Jose was directing it. I sat with the script and tried to imagine the very edges of myself, of how we in America were always trying to face each other in the truth, but couldn't. I was alone with this perspective, and while Jose "hid" his Judaism, I tried to be clinical about the conversation and get back to planning.

A meeting was set in Los Angeles for January with Diana Ross and Tracee Ellis Ross. Jose would finish shooting in Spain, then Anya would fly out, too, because he wanted her to be his assistant director. We passed dozens of emails planning the meeting, trying to find a time to talk, scheduling flights and hotels. Jose and I emailed about the meeting with the Rosses, outlined the pitch and the areas in the script that needed expansion. I also sent a note to Anya suggesting that she research being an assistant director, that the role was a difficult one, that it meant managing the flow of a shoot for the director. She thanked me for the suggestion and said she'd searched the position and she and Jose had discussed that her contract would only be for six months to make sure this was the right fit. "Well, it's his money and his time", I thought, and left it at that.

Then, I got a call from Anya.

"Something really strange happened today and I need to tell you."

I put down what I was doing. Anya had started to share with me her money problems. She'd impulsively bought a small condo with the money she'd earned working on the show for Jose, but she wanted to sell it. In order to fix that problem, she'd hired a lawyer in Bucharest, passed on to her by the doctor she'd been involved with. That lawyer settled her problems with the property she bought, but they had frozen her bank account while they did an investigation into why she had "flipped" the property so quickly. "Romania!" she'd said, "It's all so fucked up!" The freeze on her bank had left her exposed, and so I had sent her $1500 via Western Union. She'd assured me that this was common now, that everyone was using Western Union to send money during COVID, Jose had even emailed me saying he was trying to send money to me, and asked if Western Union would be okay. I'd declined, preferring a straight deposit into my account, which I sent to him with the correct SWIFT code for international transfers.

"What's up?" I asked her.

"Jose called Alonzo and Sophia to pull together some money for me."

"Okay?"

"Jose had already sent money over the limit for Western Union, so he wanted to use Alonzo or Sophia's accounts to send me $2500, but it all fell apart."

Alonso and Sophia were the stars of Jose's show. Anya had shown me pictures of them in Spain when she went to visit them. She'd also forwarded love messages from Alonso and I had received an email from him on Facebook asking if she was safe. Sophia and Anya were, I understood from Anya, growing very close. Anya could tell me in detail about their creative lives, personal experiences, and how they wanted to help her.

"What happened?" I asked, tired.

"Well, Jose called a meeting with them and they all wanted to send me some money. But then, David (Jose's business partner) came into the meeting and freaked out."

"Freaked out?"

"Yes, he said he didn't care if we all fucked each other, but that we should not involve you."

"Me?"

"Yes, Jose wanted to send you the money so you could send it to me. David said that we can't fuck with Americans, that you are all like Trump and you won't respect them if they involve you in money problems."

I was a bit baffled. I'd watched David in interviews and found him quite lucid. I thought about Trump, how we now seemed like pigs to people abroad–I was ashamed.

"He voted for Trump!" Anya exclaimed. "David thinks Trump is great, and you are going to be like him."

"I what?"

"You are like Trump."

"No, I'm not."

"Well, he sees America that way. And now he has scared them all about giving me money. What will I do?"

As Anya was talking to me, I received an email from Jose. I said I would call her back.

Jose let me know that David had really freaked out, that he'd shown how little he cared for artists during this hard time of COVID. David, Jose said, could really be an asshole, and that he was very sorry to put me in this position and that he hoped it would not jeopardize our work together. Could I please help Anya while he sorted out the mess with David?

I called Anya back and said I would wire her the $2500. She thanked me profusely. Jose emailed me a picture of a deposit he'd made to my bank with the routing number clearly showing. Alonso texted me on Facebook with thanks. I moved on from the moment, my day filled with things to prepare for the Los Angeles meetings–cleaning up the scripts, thinking of other people we needed to meet with, awaiting Jose's thoughts on moving forward, the $2500 dollars seemed to slip into a growing list of things I needed to recover, yet I was starting to feel lost.

I received an email from Jose a few days later that made me feel better. He had reviewed my background and asked if I wanted to have a contract with him to act as a strategist. I had experience helping start-ups coming from Europe to California and he suggested that I structure a new production company and help him with communications. I thought it would be a good idea, I wanted something formal and I needed a deposit to hold my time. He agreed, we drew up a year contract and he offered a reasonable amount as a monthly basis that reflected the fees for this kind of work. My lawyer reviewed the offer, tightened it up, sent it to Jose and we signed the contract. He sent me another screen shot of money deposited in Spain to my account in New York.

The day of the election was drawing closer.

In America, the mood was heavy. Every morning I would wake and turn on the news. Trump, like a broken King Lear, badgered and screamed his conspiracies, hour after hour. Biden and Trump had been "debating"–if you can call it that–on live TV, and Biden, so exasperated, had told Trump to, "Shut up, man!" This request matched the feelings of half the country while the other half was all in with Trump. The news anchors spent a lot of time talking about the "cult" of Trump. They dove into how he'd successfully "brainwashed" millions to believe him, to buy his brand, to buy his lies, to hate. How, they asked, had he shifted the focus from the facts to so many lies?

I wondered, too, who were all these Americans who believed this fabrication of an American past–"Make America Great Again"–how had that happened to us? I remembered again when Ducu died, how that new very young Director, whom he'd tapped to take over the theater had said that she wanted to "Make Bulandra Great Again." This brand of imagined greatness traveled the world and the power-hungry had leveraged it to bully and bribe and confuse people into submission.

Yes, there was a "long con" going on in the world. And I, clearly above it all, wondered how that worked. All I knew was that, I, too, had a desire to escape.

Lars watched me get more and more stressed. He asked me not to watch the news anymore, and said he couldn't handle the constant calls, emails, and texts I was getting from Europe. He'd spent his childhood living in Spain with his father in the summers, and told me that Latin culture can be very intense, but he'd had enough. Could I, would I consider measuring my contact on this project until all the payments were in? I'd assured him he was right, that I had made a mistake, that perhaps I was in over my head. Why me? Why did Jose want to work with someone untested–I'm just a theater person after all? Lars said I needed to trust my talent, that in many ways my talent was driving all of this. I looked into his face, so supportive and kind, and decided to believe him, although deep down I did not believe in myself.

The election got closer. People were voting early by the millions. So many of us were still trapped in our homes as COVID spiked during our holidays. Day by day, we got closer to the event that now threatened to cancel our life as we knew it: another four years of Trump.

The isolation was getting to me. The morning calls from Anya were tiring me. My body was getting worn down from writing. I did not like where I was, and Lars was worried.

"Please, just put down all the tech and breathe", he implored. I tried, but I was being thrown a lot of work to do by Jose–the creation of a Limited Liability Corporation, more contracts, a plan to enter the American market. I was surprised that I could write a business plan so quickly, that he allowed me to write my own vision into his–how like the times of epistolatory romances, he and I had seemed to find a flow to our writing. Back and forth, we spoke of his dream for a new kind of production company where art mattered, again.

Election Day came and we spent forty-eight hours glued to the television. Biden was tentatively named the winner, but Trump said it was rigged. The critical Georgia election for two democratic senators, one black and one Jewish, held us all rapt as it went into a runoff. I worried. And, I worried. If Trump were able to pull off a coup, would I stay in America?

I went back to *Mixed Messages* and wrote in more conflict for the characters about fleeing the United States. I imagined Diana Ross running down West Broadway during a riot. In the story, Diana takes off her coat and her scarf to give to fallen people lying in the streets and she ends up all in black–like a cultural ninja, like a protector of the streets as people who look anonymous and white, ravage the streets, killing black people as they moved down into the Jewish part of town. I saw her pound on the apartment door of her daughter, the world falling apart. My country is broken. This is all I could think:

My country has lost heart. I expressed all this to Anya, who was writing to me interested in what was happening in America. She wanted to learn more about our world because she was considering moving to the United States. Sometimes, we would watch the same news show and I would explain, as best I could. She was interested, alert. And I started to see she could, if she put her mind to it, think critically, ask some good questions and follow the thread before her.

I got a note from Jose, worried that his business partner, David, wanted to do something terrible to the *Ducu Rising* script. David wanted to turn the script into an exploration of the sex life of Ducu. David thought the story would sell better as a story about crazy artists. Jose wanted the story to be about Ducu as an artist, and to show the courage of what he lived through in Romania. I had cold feet. How could this work as an episodic series? The screenplay I had written worked as a movie, but as a series, I thought not. But the rub was that David wanted to write the series with me, and though they had bought the property, I had signed off to their language that Netflix could do with it as they wanted. I'd reviewed this with my lawyer in mind and came to the conclusion that this was industry practice, so I was stuck, I had to bend towards what David wanted.

Anxious, I asked Jose what he wanted to do about it. He said he was "in the shit" with David, trying to finish the shooting (which I saw on Instagram was happening) and that he thought perhaps he should leave the production company completely–that the trip he had to take to the U. S. would mean he was finished with Spain. It seemed severe to me, but times were crazy for the production world getting content to the streaming companies. Netflix was publicly stating they were going to increase their new films and series. Having worked at Netflix years ago, I knew they meant business. They would not stop their growth as a company, they would not stop their productions, they were buying up scripts and projects like crazy. It was a fact, in the news, talked about among my friends, so I followed Jose's lead and waited to hear what the next steps would be.

Anya called me soon after and said there was a real problem about the book of *Ducu Rising*. The publishers, now owned by another group, were refusing to pay me. She had told Jose and he had, on European time (while I was asleep) hired a lawyer for me through Anya. She was able to talk to the lawyer and they were going to get my money from the publishers because I had a solid contract that they had signed, and so they were obliged to pay. She would go for me, and they could finalize the process. Over the next weeks, she would let me know how the case was going, and while we waited, she asked for some money to support herself while she worked on my behalf. I sent her $500 I didn't have. I also got emails and calls from the lawyer in Bucharest–he had never seen this kind of problem before, he was sorry, he was on it–I should not worry. I was given the name of the judge in the case, as well as the paperwork they had filled out. I was ready for it to end. I didn't even want *Ducu Rising* in the world anymore, neither the book, nor the screenplay. I had made a mistake.

"You know, I think Ducu is punishing us." Anya said brightly. "He probably just wants to be remembered well, and this is his way of telling you."

I wished this were true. But, this isn't what he would say to me. He would tell me to listen to the mystery of life, to not get entangled in the business of art, which, he'd also say, was the end of an artist.

Christmas came and went. Jose was silent. Anya and I talked a lot on video, she was alone in her house in Bucharest, and together we talked about wanting to be free.

"Maria came to my apartment yesterday", she said, bluntly.

"Why?"

"She came with the police. She says I tried to cheat Ducu in the end."

"What?"

"Yes. She banged hard on the door and wanted me to give myself up to the police."

"What did you do?"

"Nothing. I was so sad. I still love her. I wish she respected me. But here, no one respects anyone. We all just wish history was different."

(I wished history were different, too. Mainly, I wished I could visualize Maria banging on a door. But I could not. I tossed and turned over the images of screaming in a hallway. I saw the dark passageway from the elevator to the door very clearly. I saw the scene as though I were behind the door. I could not, for the life of me, picture Maria angry.)

Then came the news that Jose was in the hospital with COVID. For the *second* time, Anya said. He was able to type and so he sent me a note saying he was okay, but would I please contact Diana and Tracee to talk to them, to make the changes in the script. He then told me he had 4.5 million dollars in an account in New York, that he would make me a signatory on it, and I could pay myself and the bills for a lawyer to help us draw up the production company. I told him not to worry, to get better–and deep down, deep, deep down I did not like the idea of being a signatory for him. This was all moving forward too fast–and then it hit me, he and I had never, not once, spoken on the phone.

(I lay in bed that morning, the morning I was true to myself and I started to breathe funny. I could not slow down my heart. I could not hear myself. I spent the rest of the day trying to sort out the many deposits that had been sent to me, and still my bank account was empty. I mentioned this to my father who told me to slow down, to wait. So, I managed my day by popping anxiety medication chased with coffee.)

The next day, I was awakened early as usual by Anya. Jose had been intubated. I felt my heart rate rise. I could not hear what she was saying. She was manic, worried, and wanted to go to Spain to see him. She'd reached out to Sophia who'd sent her money to travel. But, Sophia also said that Jose was alone. The cast and crew had learned of his plan to leave for America without them and so they abandoned him. Sophia was angry at him, and wanted to talk to me.

I received an email from Sophia saying Jose was wonderful, but could be a real shit. He could be crazy with money; and I should be careful. She said I should protect Anya from his promises, because he could let you down. Her email was written like a poem, and the syntax was interesting. She encouraged me to keep writing, but to be smart, that I was walking into a mess–but that she would be here to help.

I talked to Anya about the emails, and then I started to get emails from Sophia saying she was in trouble, that she was dipping into her addiction. The end of the series was before her and she didn't understand why Jose was not taking her to America. Since Jose was intubated…

(*Wait. Just, wait, I need to breathe.*)

Because Jose was incubated, we had to wait to see what would happen to any of it. And there was more bad news, Jose had learned that his aunt in New York had died of COVID, and he had gone into a depression the doctors felt had impacted his immune system. He was unconscious, and they were hoping to revive him in five days.

So, we waited. Anya and I talked during the morning my time, and she gathered money to get a

Visa approved for the United States, as well as to find a way into Spain–a car perhaps, to see if she could help Jose. She asked for some money to cover the costs of the Visa. I sent it to her though I urged her to wait. But she was going crazy, she said, stuck in Bucharest.

We then got news from the doctors that Jose was off the ventilator and was recovering, but they were concerned about his heart–he was having panic attacks and was terrified of being alone. Anya got him on the phone and he begged her to come, be his assistant, and help finish the shoot as his "body", and that he would call in his requests from the phone.

(Memories of theaters invaded me. I never grew up on a film set. Wasn't I a theater person? I'd always thought it was too cold on sets. You had to wear a parka everywhere; and so I had stayed in the theater until I could no longer–until I realized everyone was dead. Why the hell was I about to make movies?)

Anya bought a ticket. She had the help of Sophia who's sent her some money. Yet Sophia was acting strangely, she'd promised Anya her apartment but now was not in Madrid because her son was having problems. Anya left anyway, and sent a picture of the wing of the plane as it landed in the worst snow-storm in Spanish history. When Anya landed, she went to the apartment of Sophia, but her boyfriend was there and tried to hit on her. Disgusted, she left and went to her friend's house–it was there that she called me.

"I've made a terrible mistake."

"Where are you?"

"At a friend's house, but it's too small and I will have to sleep on the floor. Why did I come here?"

I wasn't sure myself, but if it was all as had been presented to us: Jose was sick and isolated, and before work, we were friends–that's what Jose had said–that we were forming something new, and that was sacred.

So I went on to Airbnb.com and found an apartment for Anya in Madrid. Confirming the reservation, the owner of the place contacted Anya. I sent the address to Anya and she rushed to the apartment with two bedrooms so that Jose could stay there, too, upon discharge from the hospital. Anya FaceTimed me and showed me the apartment. Yes, it was big enough for the two of them, and it looked exactly as it did online.

Yet Anya was hungry. Anya was cold. Anya had a headache. Anya needed coffee. Anya needed a hug. Anya needed sex. All the needs of Anya poured into my waking day–her wants, her feelings, her body. She asked me to coach her on how to manage a team, how to produce, how to be in the world. "I am a director, not a business person!" she said. "How will I do this for Jose?" I assured her that even the most creative person has to deal with the business of the world and work–that the most important thing you can do is connect with another person, listen, and then solve problems. "You are my teacher, Sarah. I learn so much from you."

For days, the drama continued. Sophia emailed saying she'd lost her daughter and that she'd hired a detective and found out that Anya was her daughter. Anya called me terrified that Sophia refused to come to the set, and that David wanted Anya to fix the problem since it stemmed from her relationship.

"Anya, if you are doing work for them you need a contract", I'd stated, bluntly.

"Yes, I will work on that." Anya then sent me the contract she had written up and I took a glance–it was a replica of the contract I'd drawn up with Jose. I thought, well, she must have been listening to me; she must be learning how to take care of herself.

(Right?)

Then I heard from Tracee and Diana Ross. They were concerned about Jose. They wanted a meeting with me the following week and so we set a Zoom date. They were sweet, and it was kind of a thrill to hear from them. I heard from Anya that Diana had called Jose and that they had spoken. "Jose says Diana is wonderful. So kind and ready to work, so serious. She will help you with the script while he is still sick. It's her changes anyway, so he says you should talk with her directly." I was reading Diana's memoirs and I could see how directly involved she was in her films–she loved research, she loved the writing process–she also felt like a poet, her language and syntax had a lovely flow. She was, by all accounts, charming.

Soon, Anya got David the contract and he told her she had to hire more actors for some roles, and needed a guest star. I suggested she try to get Penelope Cruz since Jose had mentioned they were friends. Anya brought the idea to David who approved it and told her to contact the agent and get it done. Anya panicked. She had no idea how to hire a superstar so I helped her compose an email to the agent and coached her on how to make an ask for talent. Anya reached out to the agent but they ignored her. She did not hear back from them for days and finally she heard from Penelope who said she'd do it for Jose, but not for David. She wanted to tell Anya more, and so they arranged to meet.

I was not sleeping by now. The emails and texts and calls came at all hours. Lars begged me to stop. I didn't know how. I was in deep and I could not see a way out.

Jose emailed me saying he had wanted to tell me for a while but had been too sick: Bob Iger, the chairman of Disney, was a close friend of his aunt. Iger had an idea for a deal–that he wanted to put 100,000 dollars down for *Mixed Messages*, as well as for a package of five films. Jose told me we had thirty-five percent of the budget for *Mixed Messages*,and that I should contact Bob Iger to discuss the details because he, Jose was still so sick. I took Bob's email and wrote to him that I was here to talk. These numbers were insane, I thought, but ready for something, anything, I got to work.

Bob Iger promptly wrote me back, saying he was thrilled to work with us, that he was worried about Jose and wanted to get him out of Madrid. He also asked me not to take the meeting with

Diana Ross and Tracee because he was "concerned", that Tracee had gone "over his head" to the CEO and asked to have me and Jose replaced or she would not do the film. He wanted her to know that he was the money and the primary producer for the project. It was Bob Iger and he was telling me what to do, so I did it, I moved the meeting and waited for the next step. But I felt strange in my body–why was Tracee so against this? Perhaps she was right? Perhaps it was the wrong director, and I was out of line writing the story? Perhaps she was right, yet how could I speak with her if she would not respond to me?

The next day, I received an email from Diana. She told me she'd had a dream about me and that she knew we were going to make art. She sent me kisses. I longed to meet her.

I reached out to my dear friend Dr. September Williams, who is a marvel. She's one of the only black bioethicists in the world with an expertise in film, as well as an author of novels and screenplays. Brought into television shows and films that are smart enough to dig deeper into ethical issues in medicine, September can advise on everything from plots to dialog, policy to ethics–major directors count on her to lead them through complicated films and I am lucky to have her as my friend. I called her to ask if she might be a consultant for *Mixed Messages* because the character I'd written for Diana was a social worker. I sent her the script and she loved it. So, I called her.

"You want what?" September asked me on the phone.

"I know, I know, it sounds crazy, but it's for Diana Ross", I said.

"Diana Ross needs a *bioethicist*?"

"Well, no. I think the project does. I think the director may not..."

"What?"

"Well, perhaps I should have brought it to a director here?"

"Baby, you *think* so? I know at least three black women directors who are ready for their Oscar and yes, indeed, perhaps you–" She stopped herself from stating the obvious. I'd made a mistake.

"I hate to ask this, to help save–"

"Well, I'm a doctor first."

"I was going to say, save my ass."

"There's that too. But, listen, I can help her with the research around what it takes to be a great social worker and the implications the screenplay makes about the conflicts in the Movement. Right?" she stated, affirmatively.

"Yes, exactly. Thank you. I'll set up a meeting."

"Listen, Sarah. Don't be surprised if this all falls through", she said, quietly.

"Why? Why would it disappear?"

"Disney? You said Disney is the producer? Honey, I've never known them to go on a limb for stories about black women. I'm just saying", and then her voice trailed off into her experience with negation.

Yet, September had nailed it–this might all slip away, and anyway, if they were taking a chance on me, a white writer on a black theme, perhaps Disney was wrongheaded and I was in big trouble.

I pulled up my boots, wrote up a contract for September, emailed Diana about September who immediately wrote me back that she would be thrilled to work with a bioethicist. I felt my stomach clench because I was alone with this project, and I was stupid enough not to wait for another director. And deep, deep down something was not right–the lack of interest in the nuances of race in America from both Jose and Anya left me unnerved. Oh boy, I was, perhaps, fucked.

So, I did what anyone would do, I watched *The Wiz*, the remake of *The Wizard of Oz* with Diana as Dorothy. I watched with longing for the edginess of the 1970s in America. The grit of it. The truth of it. The irony of the endless search on an endless yellow brick road leading to a person who is lying. I watched the film over and over again. I played Lena Horne singing "If You Believe", and knew I did not. What did I believe in, now? What was really happening?

Spain continued to blow up.

Sophia still refused to come to the set unless Anya agreed that she was her mother. David was not allowing the doctors to let Jose out of the hospital and so Anya was forced to go there, bribe a nurse, and let her in to see Jose. She had seen him for a few hours, and then she told me, "I think I am in love with him."

Jesus Christ, I thought. I'm so glad I'm not young like that anymore–to love every man you meet?

(Exhausting.)

One early morning, Bob Iger wrote, saying I needed to help Jose calm down, that he was being hysterical and that Bob was doing all he could to get him to the U. S. He convinced Jose that he would get him a house and doctor. He sent pictures of a six-bedroom home he'd found for Jose. On a group email among me, Bob, and Jose, we shared with Jose that he needed to calm down, get well, get out of the hospital, and come to the United States. Bob then wrote to me that he was very busy, that the morning was sacred for him and that I needed to handle the rest, he'd send the ticket for the U. S, but I needed to get Jose out on my own.

Jose emailed me saying he wanted to die. He said he was in love with Anya but he needed to leave Spain immediately. He would leave the next day. He was through, he had to leave Spain.

Anya was furious. Jose told her to stay in Madrid and finish the work. She wanted to leave with Jose, but he asked her to come see him to the airport the following day. Anya called me to say she took Jose from the hospital, but that David had arranged the press to be there when he left the hospital, and that David had made a statement that he was "with" Jose through this hard time. That day, more news came out on the *Hollywood Reporter* that Jose was tapped to direct a new series shooting in Los Angeles in February. I asked Anya if she knew of this; she said she'd look into it and ask Penelope whom she was meeting for lunch the next day.

I wrote to Iger that Anya had put Jose on the plane and that he was heading to L. A.

Anya asked me to coach her before her meeting with Penelope. We talked at length and discussed eye contact, honesty, and listening. We concluded that, as Anya said, “Sometimes, being honest is the only way.” She said this as though it were a revelation.

Anya called me the next day saying she’d met with Penelope who’d been exceedingly kind. Penelope had arrived on time, with no make-up on her face–a ring and a bracelet for Anya as a gift. Penelope had sat close to her, told her that Jose had called to tell her he loved Anya. Penelope had invited her to her house in Los Angeles. Anya explained that Javier (her husband, the actor Javier Bardem) and Javier’s brother were close to Jose and that they were very worried. That David had forced Jose to sign documents while ill, and now Jose was locked into a new project that would push our work out for months. Penelope gave Anya some money to get back to Romania, because Anya had had it–she too wanted to leave.

When I pressed Anya about what Penelope wanted to do about being in the last season of the show, Anya shrugged. “She does not want to do it for David, only for Jose, only for me. So, I guess she will make up her mind. Did I do well? Did I handle her correctly?”

Had she done well? What was she doing? Making friends with a star, or a person? And, why did Penelope bring her gifts? I’d only just noticed Anya obsession with trinkets and rings and bracelets. The

European women I knew tended to bring their hearts to a meeting, never gifts. It seemed odd. But, then again, all of this was crazy.

(Crazy.)

Then the calls came from Anya about David coming to the apartment, sexually harassing her, and having her followed on the streets. She was afraid for her life. So, she was running away.

Anya called me from a cab where I heard her speak Spanish to the driver. They went to the airport, but she could not get in without a ticket she now begged me to purchase. She went to a travel agent and they got her a ticket. She asked me for money again, but something made me say…no.

(No. I had no more to share. No, I was sleep deprived. No.)

Anya searched for a place to buy a ticket, then called me. "I have the ticket", she said, pissed. "But I have to stay at a youth hostel tonight. I don't even want to show you where I am. It's disgusting. I can't move. I can't breathe. Something is wrong with me."

I talked to her for a while to calm her down.

"Why am I always left alone?" Anya said. "Why am I always abused by men? Jose should have taken me with him, he's just another user. I'm going to go back to Bucharest, and that's it, I can't do this anymore. I can't do Hollywood anymore, it's too crazy!"

She held the phone close to her face. I heard her breathing. Men were cruel, she said, over and over again, life was cruel, she should just "end it!"

(End what?)

I emailed Iger about what had happened to Anya. He wrote saying that he was glad I let him know, and that he'd have a lawyer on it. But that they were waiting for Jose and would confirm when they had him there in Los Angeles.

I thought about walking away from it all. Though at the same time, I could see why Iger was interested in Jose. As he'd told me, Disney had been thinking about dramatic projects for a while, and with Disney+ (their streaming channel) they needed more content. We were to be the more European team, and, I was told, they would invest in us while also having us churn out work… churn out work… churn out work.

(Crazy.)

Iger sent me pictures of a house he wanted to rent for me and told me I should get to L. A. as soon as Jose arrived. I sent the images to my father who said I should be careful, not to get sucked into this promise, because it seemed like this was a heavy sales tactic before the deal was set. Yes, my father was right, but he never once mentioned "selling out"–but that was the language I had heard since I was a child. In the avant-garde theater of New York, there is a push and pull between integrity and success, and every artist I had known growing up had found success by rallying "outsiders" to see their work. Broadway or Hollywood openly deemed the world of "high art" to hold little appeal for a "mass audience." So, why didn't he say that to me? "You're selling out, kid"–why didn't my father simply say it to me? Wasn't I finding success in a dream I was not raised to have?

I longed to be out of it. Jose was losing his mind. Iger was great, but had passed me on to his assistant who barely wrote English. Anya was now back in Romania freaking out that Jose had left her. I wanted it to stop.

Then, Iger wrote, saying they'd picked up Jose at the airport and he had been given an operation in

Spain that he did not need. That they found drugs in his system. They had him at Cedar Sinai Hospital. And, most importantly, Iger would send a helicopter for me to come to Los Angeles…

…

He would send a helicopter for me to come to Los Angeles.

…

He would send a helicopter for me to come to Los Angeles.

…

Then, sitting on my couch, I felt my body break. I felt my feelings freeze up. I sat paralyzed and I simply knew it:

This was not real.

Awake

I held my head in my hands. I could not breathe. I was not even thinking, I was knowing.

I felt Ducu beside me. I felt him, his hand taking my hand, the way he told me, always, to tell the truth.

I walked myself to my bedroom. I sat in my bed. I held my head in my hands.

The room was tiny. But it was real. Yes, the room was real.

I called my best friend and told her that I couldn't take it anymore, that this was not real. She asked me why? I told her I could not get anyone on the phone or Zoom to talk to me. I had not seen anyone's face but Anya's. She was silent.

"What will you do?" she asked.

"Explore", I said.

I emailed Iger. I wanted a meeting with him. It was an emergency. I needed to talk with him, now.

I wrote to Jose, I asked him where he was. He did not respond.

I got an email from Iger's office, answering in broken English and I demanded to know who I was talking with. He said: "Mr. Bob" was also at the hospital, that his daughter was in an accident and that I should not push it, that Jose had already been a handful. I told the "assistant" that I thought it was very odd not to talk to Jose, or Bob. I did not budge, I wanted to know who I was talking to, I wanted to talk to a doctor to see how Jose was.

"Why!?" the assistant demanded. "Why do you need to talk to him? It's a private matter and Mr. Bob is handling it!"

"I'm his business associate and I want to know how he is. I want to know right now."

I got another email from the assistant trying to calm me down. Then, the "assistant" named Jesus, told me he'd take a computer to Jose.

Jose wrote me, calm as could be. He said he was fine. I asked him what hospital he was in. He said he didn't know. Then he told me I was asking too many questions, making it all about me. What about him, didn't I care how *he* was?

I turned off the computer, lay on the floor, and had an anxiety attack.

Later, I crawled to the bedroom, lay in bed, and told Lars (who was visiting) my fear, that this was not real.

"If it's not, it's a great story!" he said.

We laughed.

I wanted to throw up.

I tried to breathe.

I tried to sleep.

I woke to an email from Diana who asked for a Zoom so we could finally talk.

I then got a call from Anya telling me she was freaked out.

"Stop, wait", I said, "What if this is not real?"

She exploded. How could I question this? She knew Jose was real. She had been with him. He had kissed her. He said he loved her. How could I question reality?

We hung up.

I looked up the website for Jose's company in Spain. I wrote to them saying that perhaps there was identity fraud going on. I sent them the email address for Jose. I sent the contracts.

I went back to the living room and lay on the floor.

What if nothing was real?

The next morning, Anya called, saying she would support me in any way. She was sorry. "We must get to the True!" she cried. "I always support your True."

When we hung up, I emailed Robert Chapek, CEO of Disney. Iger's assistant had given me the email with the information that Chapek wanted to talk with me.

Anya called again, saying she had gone to a lawyer and was terrified. She had been the only person to give me the information, make the connections, and handle the money, so she looked guilty. She said the lawyer said I was right to be upset and doubtful, that my writing could have been stolen this way. She was panicked that Jose had played us. I said it was not normal not to have FaceTime or see all the contracts. She agreed and hung up, despondent.

I got another email.

(*No, it would not stop.)*

Jose was furious with me. He was writing, he told me, from the hospital. Anya would not talk to him. He loved her, and that meant more to him than work. He questioned my loyalty. He questioned my honor.

I asked him to call me.

He would not.

I told him he might not be real.

He said he was.

He said I might have ruined his life, that he was going to leave the hospital and go to Anya.

Anya wrote, saying that Jose was coming to Romania. She assured me he was real, and that when he got there they could call me, but that really, he needed to prove to *her* that he loved her.

Jose emailed, saying he didn't want to work with me, that he wished me well and that Iger liked me and my work.

Anya called, saying Jose was hysterical, but she was trying to calm him.

I laughed alone in my apartment.

I was laughing at just how bad this play had become.

I decided to be like a cat and toy with the mice.

I wrote Chapek at Disney and apologized for my email–perhaps, I said, there had been some identity fraud.

That evening, Lars and I drove down the coast. I wept in the car, out of shame, out of fear. He said no matter what the truth was, he loved me, he wouldn't leave–it was going to be fine, we would get through it.

After dinner, I received an email from Jose with a picture of palm trees in Los Angeles. He said he was feeling better, that he was calm and only wanted us to be happy and to work, that he'd been through so much. I sent him a picture of the ocean water in Northern California, this person on the other end, this lack of reality, and I wished him a good night.

I hadn't noticed he'd sent me a poem/letter earlier asking why I'd upset Anya, why I didn't believe him, why I'd broken our trust. He made a prayer to the universe to save him from his own lunacy. He told me he only wanted Anya. He told me not to respond, that this was a call to the universe–for help.

I received two emails during the next two days, one was from Jose's office in Spain confirming that the email for Jose and the contracts that Jose had signed were not their contracts, and they weren't signed by Jose. Then I received an email from Disney's worldwide security team saying they'd been alerted to my email by Chapek, that Iger's name had been falsely represented. The security contact at Disney asked me to send him examples of emails, documents, and anything else I could share. I looked up his name, and saw that he was in fact from Disney. He quickly responded that, yes, all of the emails and content were fake, and that I should contact the FBI immediately.

(Lies.)

Learning all of this, I fell apart. Nothing in my life for two years had been real.

I stopped eating for five days and lay in bed, paralyzed.

Anya called me. She had been told by her lawyer that she should break contact with me. She sent me more pictures of bank deposits for me. She told me she had a good lawyer who had asked her directly if she had made it all up–and she had assured the lawyer she had not. She was so convincing, yet she spoke in the third-person, set apart from this present moment. She continued to paint a story for me where she was at the center, misunderstood. She said I would turn against her, that I would see her as the culprit. This, she said, was normal, and then she wished me well.

I never spoke with her again.

Jose emailed me pictures of bank deposits for me. He said he didn't want to know me anymore. He wanted his name off the LLC I had set up. He wanted distance from someone who was so disloyal.

Looking at the flurry of emails, I saw the patterns, the hysteria–I'd gotten lost in this.

Then the harder truth bubbled into me–Anya had made it *all* up.

There was no book. There was no publisher. There were no lawyers in Bucharest. There was no

Adrian. There was no daughter of Adrian. There had never been a publishing liaison. There was no Netflix show that Anya had been hired to be in. There was no Jose. There was no David. There was no Sophia. There was no Penelope. There was no Javier. There was no documentary in the Middle East. There was no problem between Jose and David in Spain. There was no aunt of Jose. His mother had not died. His aunt, not real, had not died. There was no *Mixed Messages* film. There was no Diana Ross. Diana Ross had never written to me in the mornings. There was no Tracee Ellis Ross. There was no Bob Iger. There was never an assistant to Bob. There was no house in L. A. There was no *Waves* film. There was no final production in Spain for Jose. There was no Anya as an assistant director–or director–or actress. I'd not connected with Anton when I was in Bucharest. Maria and I had *no* conflict. There was no awareness of me when I went to Bucharest. No one, not a soul, knew I'd been there to research a book. Anya and Ducu hadn't been engaged. She was never pregnant with his child. That was not Ducu's apartment. Those were not his clothes. Those were never his cats. His books and music were elsewhere. This was not his earring in my ear.

I had been mourning a lie. I had never said goodbye and Ducu's memory was stuck in a lie I had not even begun to understand.

In Jewish life, you take a year to really mourn. You are expected to feel deeply. You are expected to be real about it. Many people cover their mirrors to remain centered in their feelings, not in their daily lives. At the end of your year of mourning, you go back, lay a gravestone, place a rock to symbolize the earthly reality of death, and then return to yourself. Living Anya's lie, I'd stayed in a make-believe world of activities and plans. I hadn't really mourned Ducu, my dear friend, my love–and in this way, I had not really been all there for Lars.

Worse yet, in Anya's lie, I was vapor, I was–along with Maria–the woman who did not deserve his love, for she, Anya, had won a little girl's battle to manage "Daddy" to his death. It was Freudian and it was Tolstoyan and it was all bad theater, no subtext of feelings, only desperate actions for someone trapped in her mind.

For seven days, I could not get out of the bed before eleven a.m. I awoke in a panic attack, and so I took anxiety medication and Cannabis gummies to get through the day. All the emails and telephone calls of the past year ended. Anya, simply, strategically, went away. And then, the shame arrived.

In Silicon Valley, "turning out the lights" is a common occurance–when the business doesn't fly, you have to shut it down, and the higher up in the company you are, the more likely you will physically have to turn off the lights on your way out the door. So, that's what I did. I focused on the truth of it, the reality, and emailed my lawyer, the accountant, the PR team I had wanted to hire, and the banker. I had to thank them for their support, and apologize, saying there was no money to pay them for their work. I was mortified. I was embarrassed and I was anchorless, adrift, and the storm kept raging.

It took me a week to fill out the FBI documents. I had to gather all the banking exchanges, the timeline, the false emails and telephone numbers, the contracts and the offers for more business, more money, more fame. I compiled all of it and sent the documentation to the FBI. I pressed send and felt nothing.

Something the FBI wrote stuck with me–that they had so many identity fraud cases that it could take a while to see my case through. So many cases? I felt in that moment how the world was glutted, and gutted, by the disease of social media, the meta-story of it all compressed in text messages, posts, and emojis. We had become a world sick with so much–politics, plague, falseness of self, falseness of identity, falseness of being. Perhaps Anya was just another person controlled by the technology of falsity–perhaps she was in the sickness itself?

I got an email from the owners of the house in Spain where Anya had stayed. They asked me (because it was my account) to consider paying the three-month extension she had asked for, but she had fled in the middle of the day. Had I heard from her? Why had she extended and then left? What were they to do with the contract she had made with them to stay longer? All I could think was that this might be the one real thing she had done, gone to Spain, spent her days trying to fit in, hoped to stay longer–but could not. Had she gotten ahead of herself in her fiction? Had she made up the attacks by "David" to help herself get out of the mess she had made–an imaginary job, imaginary production, imaginary friends, imaginary life? I remembered her calls to me from restaurants and places in Madrid. She would report to me her meals. Had she always eaten alone? Did she know anybody there? Had she made the trip an adventure inside a lie? Was each place she ran to a new stage to rehearse, no, perform her ability to survive?

Against my will, I started to think Anya was the best actress I had ever seen. Well, a master of method acting, the technique where you become your role, become something other than yourself. Not only that, she'd done hours of research to respond to my lawyer and agent. She'd read my scripts and learned about the current state of business in the entertainment field. On top of that, she'd invented a judicial system, a special court for artists in Bucharest, and represented me in an imaginary court. She was all the pieces of a broken and lost production. She was, just as she'd told me, a romantic lost in a world of people who did not understand her need for an amazing plot. Now it overtook me, the movies she liked, the actresses she wanted to be–all of it sentimental, like a girl's favorite fantasy about princesses and happiness.

Now it flooded me, deeper into the wet loss of time, that she had been to "art school" (in her mind) with Ducu, and to "entertainment school" with me. We had been her teachers. We had been her obsession. We had led her toward knowing herself, but only within the reflection of ourselves. This seemed infinitely sad, that she could only know herself when she lied–that she could only be a bit player, an extra, because she was never truly revealed.

I soon learned that Anya had been an extra in one of Ducu's plays when she was around eighteen. She'd never made it to the main stage of one of his plays, and she'd never made it to the main stage of his life. So, too, she'd been an extra in my life, but she found a way to build herself a bigger role.

I was, on many levels, pretty fucking impressed.

Yet sleeping had become impossible. I needed to lie completely still or I could not bear the sound of my own breathing. I kept the phone by my bed but I was relieved it was silent. I looked at the empty ceiling and thought only of my own darkness–the pull of it downward into my own lost feelings lying dead after two years of a lie in the base of my body.

Lars held my hand all night. He was the only touchstone to what was real, and by listening to his breathing, I found the cadence of night. Knowing I would have to be my own person someday again, I kept trying to get the rest I knew I would need to fight.

I woke and googled Anya again on my phone. An article came up with her picture. She'd been interviewed by a glossy magazine in Bucharest, which had exposed that she'd been stalking a famous Romanian athlete. She'd given them a full interview about their love affair, how he'd looked at her and loved her immediately, how she'd followed him to where he trained and waited patiently for him to come home where she had a private practice as a psychiatrist. The athlete was mortified, stating he had no idea who she was, that he'd never met her, and that she followed him everywhere. The journalists mentioned how convincing she was, and ended the article with a doctor's saying Anya seemed to be suffering from "delusional disorder."

Anya seemed to have consistent themes: she was abandoned as a child but grew up in a small village. She was a "smart" person in a world no one understood. She was loved by powerful men who could not give her what she needed. She was willing to drop everything for love. She would fight to the death for a man–to depend on her. These themes carried themselves through her stories about Ducu, the doctor, Jose, and the athlete. She could disappear into her stories, and with me she had played all the roles.

How had she done it? Lars thought it would cost hundreds of thousands of dollars to pull off a scam like this, and for what? I'd not given her my life savings. She had just wanted–what? Attention? Could it have been that simple? Alone, she had produced the play, but I had written it? Alone in Romania, no future, no training as an artist, she'd wanted to move me and those I love around like set pieces in a play? She played all the parts, but changed all the syntax? Measured all the plots and cut out a starring role for herself at every turn? "Masterful" said Lars, "And, terrifying."

How had I fallen for it? I'm pretty smart, and a pretty good read of people. At least that's what I have been told. Though none of that mattered when I was grieving, in my wanting a better outcome for Ducu's life, for my life, for our collective lives. Nothing prepared me for the production Anya had created. Nothing prepared me for my own ability to ignore the facts. Nothing, not even a happy ending, could have protected me from my own ability to lie–to myself. She was everything and everywhere in my life, she had built the sets and invented the plot and then had played me like a fiddle.

Though I had no proof that she had played all the roles. Perhaps Peter was in on it? Perhaps it took a team to do days and days of business emails, research on budgets and contracts, creation of emails and storylines. To think of it, perhaps all those text messages Peter showed me of Ducu's last days might have been from Anya. Had she been playing Peter, too? What if it had all started there, that she had convinced Peter that she was Ducu's protector and had set him up with a false dialog with Ducu? Perhaps he was a victim, too?

I thought of an idea Anya had had that I had thought was interesting. Anya said Jose had approved this idea she had for a story about an actress who gets lost in her roles and goes crazy. "Did I ever tell you", she'd said only a few weeks earlier, "how I went mad in acting school? I had played a role and then they had to put me in the shower because I was having convulsions? I could not act because I could not leave the role." I had taken that as a technical fact, and had drawn up an idea for project, which I called *The Actress*. The story was of a well-known actress in Romania who–on the eve of the Romanian revolution in 1989–runs away to East Berlin and finds refuge in Bertolt Brecht's theater. There, the actress, who remains nameless, flees from East Berlin to Paris, and scrapes the ground in other theaters to finally land in Hollywood. I grappled with the ending. Yet it was Anya who said, "Promise me you will kill her off?"

"Kill her?"

"Yes, she has to die. She has no reality. She has no meaning."

That conversation haunted me. She was nothing to herself, this Anya, this character in her own play. She had no subtext, she had no voice. She was a "nobody" in a world of people she longed to be. And I had felt like this before–alone, not seen, and with Ducu I had been frustrated after sending him email after email the last year of his life. I could see he read them but not respond. Anya had used that with me, she had told me that she too found his isolation frustrating, that she had gone to his house and screamed at him to stop drinking, that she singularly had convinced him to take care of himself, that *she* had won.

I had to shake my head with that memory. I'd once felt relieved knowing that I was not the only one who could not get through to Ducu, that she had confirmed how he had wanted to disappear from the world. Though I still had no idea why he wanted to become nothing, to only focus on his last play–and then, like a wisp, lift away from us into death. He'd almost seemed relieved. I had no clearer idea why he did that today than I had two years ago, and deep down, I felt I never would. I would never know what part of his memory she thought would be destroyed, I would never understand the silence around his life at his theater, I would never be able to write about the reality of his death, except that it happened, and that he in the end seemed to want to disappear from the world. His death was his own, and I had to accept that weightless fact, intact.

So I did what I should have done from the beginning, I wrote to Maria. I pulled up my Facebook and laughed. I was back to where I had started, reaching out to a virtual person as my virtual self. I wrote with shame, I wrote with grief and longing, still for her, for this person who had been one of the most important people to Ducu, and I begged forgiveness. I told her I was here in the world. I told her I wanted to connect if she could. I told her I sent love.

Weeks previous, there had been a violent insurrection in the American Capitol and people had died, lawmakers had been hunted by Trump supporters who wanted to hang them. We had been weeks away from swearing in our new president and the news programs were airing interviews with those who had invaded Washington D. C. The people who spoke with the press expressed their love and devotion to Trump, manically convinced they were doing a noble thing. They were saving the country, and sometimes people had to die to change the world. It was madness, they were crazed, we watched with wonder. How did people get to this place, to be led away from the truth, to fall into this virus of "alternative facts", into danger?

I knew how, I was one of them. Though set on a different path, I was capable of falling into a lie.

But why? I knew what any good therapist would ask me, "What was in it, this experience, for you?"

In the silence, in the sound of the sea outside my windows, with no texts flashing on my phone, I knew what had been in it for me. I hadn't had to face death. Ducu's death. My aging. Time flying and not coming back. All this noise had redirected my truth. All this drama had allowed me to create a world where I "understood" Ducu's last days. The story Anya had told me, that he'd lied about going to England to direct a play and had gone to the hospital alone to die–that lie that had given me a feeling he'd been free at the end of his life. Yet I'd known, deep down, something had been wrong. When so many of the people in Bucharest said that Ducu's memory was being forgotten, that he was disappearing, that the theater was gone, I knew there was some truth in that–so why were so many people speaking about him as though he had vanished long before his death? What had happened? Why would nobody tell me the truth? Why had people mentioned Liviu Ciulei every time I had asked about Ducu at his very end? They all told me Ciulei had been disappointed at his end, that even after he had made Bulandra the famous home to artists he had felt alone–he had died in Germany, disconnected from Romania–he had felt history did not hold him, and he died abroad. Was the Bulandra haunted? Was the theater itself stuck in a history it could not resolve? Had Ducu been trapped in the end, confused, and unable to exist in the world?

And then I felt it, how the grave of Ducu is not the only home of Ducu. People believe that he haunts the Bulandra, blowing out lights in the stairwells and flicking the light board switches in the main hall. People around the world speak of his presence and memory. He seemed to float between the words of people who'd only just realized what they have lost.

Overwhelmed, two years of lies escaping my body all at once, I fell back into my bed and slept and I had a dream–a dream so long and involved I lived an entire life in a forest of Ducu's ghosts.

ACT 4

"What would your good be doing if there were no evil, and what would the earth look like if shadows disappeared from it? After all, shadows are cast by objects and people. There is the shadow of my sword. But there are also shadows of trees and living creatures. Would you like to denude the earth of all the trees and all the living beings in order to satisfy your fantasy of rejoicing in the naked light?"

—Mikhail Bulgakov,
The Master and Margarita

A Dream of Trees and Television and Ghosts

Trees like tall bodies line the River Dambovita, which flows into the Arges River, a tributary of the Danube. Below the water, lie bodies, long dead and all the products of history–they create the riverbed with random bones floating to the top. Bucharest is before me, the light ambient as though a thousand theatrical bulbs are held up by a patient god.

The trees sway, long and elegant. Yet the wind is so loud I can hear it pound against the bark. Ducu walks quickly along this river, his scarf thick and long. He pushes against the wind. He pushes against the rain pouring down on one side of the river where there is only sunlight on the opposite side.

I am about ten feet behind him with a fifties-style handheld camera. I must stop to wind the camera, though it slips from my hands as I try to keep up with his pace. I look at his back and I can hear him muttering, "Stupid!" He says to himself, "Stupid! Stupid! Stupid!" He continues to pound his feet against the damp cement, never ceasing to berate himself.

Now he stops in front of a building. It looks as though it should be a cheese shop, or a bookstore, or a pet store, yet in this moment it is a theater. Ducu pounds on the door, he screams. I cannot hear what he is saying. I walk closer, shooting film of his now even more aggravated back. He screams on.

"I know you are in there! I know you are hiding! Why don't you come out? Why don't you?" Ducu stops, pounds the door again. He goes to the large floor-to-ceiling window, presses his hands against the glass, and peers in. Nothing, he sees nothing. Frustrated, he stands back, looks into the window at his reflection. "What do you want from me? What the fuck do you want?!" Then with a fierce gesture he screams at himself in the window as he pulls one earring out of his right ear, and throws it against his reflection. The glass cracks, giving off the sound of unending shattering. He backs away. He pivots. I follow.

Down more streets he now runs, his coat, no a cape, yes, a cape, floating behind him. The rain is always to his left, the sun to his right. He darts back along the river, making his way to the oldest part of the town. People, like a thick wave, walk in front of him blocking his way. He pushes hard and the people in the street push back against him. Then, he stops.

I watch as Ducu turns slowly to look into another storefront. He takes a long, deep breath and then repeats himself, presses his hands against the door, bangs and screams that he knows they are hiding and that he does not know what they want from him. Then he pulls out an earring and throws it at his own image, shattering that glass. I follow him through the city. He repeats this screaming until he looks exhausted. He's pulled all the earrings from his ears. He's now thrown off his coat in front of the Bulandra, and swerving, he opens the door to enter the lobby, and yells, "Well, at least *this* fucking door works!"

The lobby is filled with women. They sit suggestively, their legs exposed. They lie on couches, large chairs, piles of pillows, and one trampoline. Ducu sees the women and is set immediately into a new mood. He smiles. He reaches for his cigarettes. He pulls his hand over his mouth, moving the small beard around his lips. He winks.

"Come and sit with us!" they coo. Some move their hands against the fabric they are lying on.

Some lean back and arch their heads backwards. Some put fingers to their lips and blow kisses. "So many of you! So many choices!" He scratches his head. He rolls his eyes like a silent movie star–the fact of their near nudity delighting him. They giggle. He pretends his hand is shaking as he lights up–the cigarette darts about like a wand.

"If you'll all wait here, I will be right back. I'll be just a moment! I have to direct a play and it won't take but a minute." Ducu touches a woman's face; it is soft. He leans over to kiss her but she dissolves. Ducu, confused, turns to the other women. "What's going on?"

All the women roll to one side or the other, and purr, "We're going to fuck you."

"What?!" he demands, interested.

"Not literally", they continue. "We are in your theater now. We are the tempest and the future. We guard the gates of this place and won't let anyone in–we will keep everyone away from you. Trust us! We love you. We'll fuck you." The women shift in shape, becoming a mural, one that has been painted too quickly, the paint not yet dry.

Ducu takes them in, puts his hand to his hip, looks at them again, and says, "I don't need you."

"Yes, you do", they say. "You can't do a thing without us. You can't open a letter. You can't even breathe. We are here now–we have our eyes on you–go direct your play, but don't forget, we are the main characters now."

At this comment, Liviu Ciulei, the great director, the master and ghost of the Bulandra, stands by Ducu. His silver hair gleams. His suit looks worn, as though he has had to crawl through mud. Putting his hand on Ducu's shoulder, he sighs with a cigarette hanging from his lips. "My boy", he pleads. "What a mess you've made."

"Mess? Look at them, they're gorgeous!"

"Ducu, you get distracted."

"I don't…"

"You do. You have. You're–"

"Discrete!"

"My boy, it's not about that. There is danger around you and you don't see it. Tell me, do you even know what time it is?"

"I never know what time it is."

"Well, then how can you know if you are not in danger? 'Theater time' is not 'life time'–you're in a dream. You're in a dream you've created. You–"

"Am I dead?"

"Well, not on stage. We are all dead after directing too much Shakespeare."

"What?"

"Yes. No one tells you this, but Shakespeare makes you think he has his own reality, when in fact it is the *only* reality."

"That's what I have been telling people!"

"Listen", Ciulei says, leaning into Ducu's ear. "We have a television show to do now, but afterwards I am going to tell you the secret. You're not going to like it, and it will make you feel you've been wrong this whole time, searching and searching, but I think it will ease your pain a bit."

"That sounds wonderful." Ducu whispers back. "This search *is* exhausting."

"Yes, I know. Come, we're going to be late and that is something *I* don't like to be." Ciulei says this in a pointed way. Ducu rolls his eyes.

Ducu puts his hand on the old man's back. When he does, dust floats around them. It is the dust of every theater they have ever been in, and now it rises, surrounds them, and follows them into the main hall.

The theater is its blue self. All the red Ciulei once adored is stripped away and everything, including the chairs, is painted blue. Ivy crawls up the walls. There is dirt on the floor. It is a garden of Ducu's own making. Ducu raises his hands as though conducting an opera. Music soars from the empty seats, and he walks down the aisle keeping perfect time with an opera that no longer makes sense. Ciulei stops Ducu from conducting. “We have visitors.” And nods his head towards the stage.

Television cameras have appeared on the stage. Candles are lit, small votives line the edges, and four chairs have appeared. A man, small but finely dressed with long hair and high boots, sits rolling a cigarette. “Who is that?” Ducu asks Ciulei.

“Can’t you see?” Ciulei asks, incredulous. “He’s here to do the interview.”

“Yes, but who is it?”

“Well, Molière.”

“What the fuck is Molière doing here?”

“He’s not in production so he’s here, I asked him. He is very nice.”

“But”, Ducu whispers. “What am I to tell *him?* Of all people? He’s a bit of a god!”

“You always exaggerate. He’s just a guy. A guy who writes. Come on, we’re late!”

Ducu and Ciulei take hands and walk down the aisle towards the stage. Molière stands, lights his cigarette, and waves, “Look! Directors! What fun this will be!”

Ducu looks around the theater. There are no people in the seats, but we hear the mulling of candy wrappers, paper moving, people coughing. The sound of an audience hits Ducu, and nervous, he sits in his appointed seat. It is Ciulei, Molière, and Ducu–and one empty seat.

"Who's that for?" Ducu asks the men.

"Elijah, of course!" Molière proclaims. "Don't be so nervous, boy. We're just going to have a little chat."

At this, the lights shift and a producer emerges from stage left. "And in, 5, 4, 3, 2…" and he gestures "1" with his finger. The cameras point towards Molière. Ducu looks confused.

"And we are back! Welcome to 'Molière and Me' a show where we search for the meaning of life, love, and how to die dramatically with theater artists who really knew how to live!" Molière speaks to the television camera. "With me tonight are two very promising directors, M. Liviu Ciulei and M. Alexandru Darie. May I call you Ducu?"

"Yes, um, please." Ducu settles into his chair, his knee shaking.

"Very good! Ducu, tell me, when did you first read *me*?"

"Oh!" Ducu shifts to think. "I didn't. I saw you. I saw a play and I laughed and laughed."

"Very good! And, tell me, how old were you?"

"Very young. It was during Ceaușescu's reign."

"Uh huh…" Molière looks bored.

"Yes, it was very hard then. We had no food."

"Whatever…Liviu? When did you first read *me*?"

Ciulei, impatient, swats dirt from his mud-stained pants and shrugs as though he could care less.

"You don't like *me*?" Molière smiles.

"I thought we were here to talk about our theater? Bulandra. This one", Ciulei almost barks.

"Right, well, I'm just giving our audience what they want. That is important. Give them what they expect in the beginning, then hit them hard with the truth. Right, boy?" he says, clear-eyed, to Ducu.

"Yes, sir. Of course", Ducu says.

"Very good. My next question is about love. Ducu?"

"Yes, sir?"

"Please, call me Jean-Baptiste."

"No! I couldn't."

"Please do."

"Jean-Baptiste."

"Yes, tell me about love. Have you had it?"

"Yes, a few times–but, why?"

"Because directors fall in love often…"

At this, Ciulei interrupts with a cough, "Rubbish", he mutters.

"Why?" Molière smiles.

"We love the stage most of all", Ciulei says, emphatic, annoyed.

"Not entirely", Ducu adds. "I have loved deeply, but it confuses me. All the feelings and no place to put them…there is no stage for love."

"Yes, where to put them." Molière offers, shaking his head.

"Rubbish", Ciulei repeats. "This is all cliché. Directors are humans with a skill to make other worlds onstage. That is what we should be talking about!"

We hear rustling, a commotion, the sounds of audience movement. "Excuse me!" We hear. "*Excuse me*!"

Molière puts up his hand to shield his eyes as he looks past the lights into the audience. "Yes? Who is that?"

"It me!" a woman says.

"Who?"

"The person who should really be up there!"

"Show yourself!" Molière bellows.

"Why?! It's always men, men, men talking about themselves and their sex and their lives… why did I found all this? For you to hog the stage?"

"Oh, don't tell me Feminism has come to Romania?" Molière retorts.

"Well!" The woman states, "That would mean humanism has arrived! Correct?"

Ducu puts his hand to his eyes now. He peers forward. He leans forward, "Mrs. Bulandra?"

Madame Lucia SturdzaBulandra now stands in the audience, a hot spotlight emerges behind her.

"Ducu!" She points a finger at him. "I left all this to you!"

Ducu gasps at Madame Bulandra, the founder of the Bulandra Theater.

"What about me?" Ciulei says.

"I left it to you first, Liviu, then to Iordanescu and then this one, this Ducu, this monster!"

"Monster? What makes me a monster?" Ducu responds, hurt.

"Have you found your mother?" she says.

"Oh, now we are getting *Freudian*??" Molière bellows.

"No", Madame Bulandra says, calm, focused, fully illumined from behind. "Did he find her? Has he been looking? Did he name a hall in her honor? Did he reconcile the past?"

"I have no idea. I am here to talk about this theater, not about the lost little boys in us", Molière interrupts.

"Let her finish, please. Madame, what was I supposed to do?" Ducu pleads.

"You passed the theater on to a young girl? Why?" she demands.

"I wasn't well. I was…"

"What?!" Ciulei shouts. "You passed it on without discussing it with us?"

"You see!" Madame Bulandra says. "A monster!"

"No, you see, I think a woman should be in charge of a theater", Ducu pleads.

"I agree!" Ciulei says.

"Oh, hell, I do, too. At least theoretically", Molière says.

"Yes", Ducu says to Madame Bulandra. "What was I supposed to do?"

"Make a wide search!" Madame Bulandra pleads. Open the doors, boy. Invite us all, all the women in."

"Get to your point, *woman"*, Molière says.

"He grew distracted!" Madame Bulandra continues. "He did not listen to his better angels. He did not know how to be kind to himself, and now he is gone."

"This is very sad", Molière says to a camera.

"Yes, very!" Madame Bulandra says, anguished. "Ducu, what do you have to say for yourself?"

And then there is the hysterical laughter of women coming from the last seats in the theater.

"Who dares laugh?" Madame Bulandra says.

Two women stand, one is small and the other grand. They have their arms wrapped around each other and cannot stop their laughter, deep and earthy.

“Stop!” Madame Bulandra says.

“What a waste of time trying to get a man”, one woman says, “and a director at that, to understand!”

“Yes! Let him go”, the other woman says. “He is just a child!”

“Oh, for god’s sake, who is that?” Molière stands, stomps, a foot and sits back down.

“It is I.”

“And, it is I!”

“Merde”, says Molière, looking at Ciulei and Ducu. “They love to follow me around. In life they competed, in death they haunt me!”

“Oh, relax!” one of the women says.

“Well, show yourself then, always hiding in the back!” Molière motions with a frustrated hand as the women, arms still around each other, make their way toward the stage.

“This is what happens when your star gets too big.” Molière points at them.

“Jesus Christ!” Ducu says. “Is that?” Ducu holds his hands up over his eyes to block the spotlights that now shine upon the women.

“Jesus Christ has nothing to do with it”, we hear one of the women say, as they giggle and now stand preparing to smoke cigarettes by the exit sign.

"Yes, yes." someone says, faking boredom. "Bernhardt and Rachel–always standing around with commentary."

"Sarah Bernhardt? And,*Rachel*? I thought I heard you when I lived in Paris. In a theater, late at night", Ducu pleads.

"Yes, that was us", Rachel says, flatly, her white Greek tunic draped suggestively around her shoulders.

"Why didn't you talk with me then?" Ducu says.

"Darling, you weren't dead", Bernhardt says.

"We only like the dead. The living have too many questions and there is no way to give a proper autograph anymore", Rachel says.

"Amazing!" Ducu says, now leaning forward in his chair, charmed by the women. "How do you like my theater?" He winks.

"Oh, look, he's flirting!" Madame Bulandra huffs, disgusted.

"Lucia, don't be such a fucking prig!" Bernhardt huffs back.

"So, he loves life? Who cares? Let him flirt", Rachel says.

"This is serious! We're having a real conversation about his mistakes", Madame Bulandra almost begs.

"Mistakes? You are trying to convince this one of his mistakes? What a waste of time, darling. See, Rachel, what did I tell you, she has no idea how to run a theater." Bernhardt has one hand on her hip.

"Here we go…" Molière rolls his eyes.

Madame Bulandra is so hurt and shocked she cannot speak. She sits, devastated.

"Be nice, please", Ducu implores the women while grinning ear to ear watching the scandal before him.

"Oh, we're very nice. We just want to say a few words", Rachel says, turning her back to Madame Bulandra. "M. Darie, please be advised that we have done an audit of your life's work and wish to inform you–"

"God, here comes the bureaucracy!" Molière wails.

"We wish to inform you…" Bernhardt picks up the slack while staring Molière down. "We wish to inform you that you did a poor job hiding your Jewishness."

Ducu looks blank. "I have no idea what–"

"Please", says Rachel, one hand trying to get her lighter to work. Bernhardt takes the lighter and lights Rachel's smoke. Rachel smiles as she takes a deep drag. "Yes, if you look at the body of your work, you can see how Jewish you are. We should know, we hid out for centuries. This one…" Rachel gestures towards Bernhardt. "She was in total denial."

"I was", Bernhardt says, now lighting her own cigarette.

"I have no idea what you…" Ducu laughs nervously. "We think my mother was–"

"Please." Rachel lifts her free hand to stop him. "Not your usual spiel. Look, in death we come clean. Okay?"

"We do?" Molière says.

"Jean-Baptise, *please*", Bernhardt says. "And what kind of television show is this? There aren't enough chairs and my leg is killing me."

"I didn't even invite you! This happens all the time with you two!" Molière stands as though an audience is applauding, then sits back down.

Rachel and Bernhardt look at each other and scoff. They take long drags off their cigarettes. "You want to tell him?" Rachel asks Bernhardt.

"No, you go ahead. I like how you say it." Bernhardt limps to the side of the stage and leans against it. Ducu jumps up and brings Bernhardt his last pack of cigarettes. "Thanks, baby." She nods to him, and he sits again at attention.

"This is a farce", Molière mumbles.

"Well, farce is *not* the absence of truth, so I will continue!" Rachel says as Ciulei nods his head in agreement. "M. Darie, after careful consideration, we want to encourage your next production."

"I get another production?" Ducu asks her, surprised.

"Well, yes, it is your job, correct?" Rachel smiles. "Let me continue. Our committee wants to encourage you to explore your roots a bit more deeply. You tend to focus on the political, but ignore the interconnectedness, the, dare I say, intersectional reality of your inner life and the feminized medium theater offers. M.Darie, dig a bit deeper, be a bit bolder, don't hold back from your heritage and hide in plain sight. We are living in dangerous times and we need to be proud of who we are, especially in death. I mean, in death you get a chance to re-cast your life, hang new scenery to your memory and once and for all ask the question, 'What's Christ got to do with it after all?'"

There is silence in the hall. All the ghosts look to Ducu who sits with his legs crossed, a new cigarette lit from nowhere, his hands quiet. "Where were you when I needed you?" he asks the ghosts, sadly.

"We have been waiting for you", Rachel says, sweetly.

At this, there is a loud thud and the doors from the lobby swing open. It is Anya, wrapped dramatically in old cloth she seems to have found backstage and has gathered in a messy clump. Waving her arms like a dramatic actress searching for words, she puts her hand to her head and screams out, "Oh! My love!"

"Who is that?" says Molière.

"This is getting interesting!" Bernhardt says, moving to stand next to Rachel by the exit sign.

"Oh my darling!" Anya wails, moving down the aisle toward the men. Posing, she looks at Ducu, "My love! I am here!"

Looking at Molière, Ducu says, "Is she with you?"

"No!" Molière says, his eyes glued to the performance before him.

"Is she with you?" Ducu asks Ciulei.

"Good God, no." Ciulei also stares.

"Don't you recognize me, Darling?" Anya says, climbing on the chairs to get Ducu's attention. "I am here to save you!"

"Get out! Out!" Madame Bulandra barks, shooing Anya, who wails and holds on to the wall.

"Darling!" Anya screams.

"Go! Fiend! No groupies here!" Madame Bulandra now drags the weight of her own skirt and pushes along the seats. Terrified, Anya recognizes her. "But I am an actress! I am a director! I am here to save him!"

"Go! Flee!" Madame Bulandra waves her arms and ten "techies" dressed in black emerge, grab Anya by the arms and pull her screaming from the theater, "I love you! I am your biggest fan! I'm your biggest fan!" Anya bellows as the doors slam behind her.

There is silence in the theater as the ghosts try to collect their thoughts.

"But that was brilliant!" Bernhardt declares, collecting her skirts, and hobbles quickly up the aisle. "What talent!"

"Not again!" Rachel says, charging after Bernhardt. "Sarah, you always fall for the crazy ones!"

With this, Rachel and Bernhardt run through the doors after Anya into the lobby. We hear from far away Rachel pleading, "Sarah! Stop falling for crazy!"

The remaining ghosts look around and shrug.

"Was she with me?" Ducu asks Madame Bulandra.

"No! But she is a part of the problem", Madame Bulandra says, looking to make sure no one will interrupt her as she walks out of the audience down toward the stage.

"I don't understand any of this. It's just dreadful theater politics!" Molière lights another cigarette. "This is why theaters fail. They fail when people can't see that it is all ephemeral–leadership means nothing without writers!"

"Oh, shut up, Jean!" Madame Bulandra states.

"Jean-*Baptiste*, thank you very much!" Molière says, haughtily.

"Pfft!" Madame Bulandra waves him off. "Ducu. You left it all in a mess. You walked away from your body. You gave your blood but did not think to ask for help. You didn't find her. Ducu! Are you listening to me?"

Ducu covers his eyes and seems to weep. The others are silent. There is only the sound of his breathing, long but shallow. Slowly, a backdrop of trees floats down behind the men. They seem to sway. Ducu swerves as he stands, the light behind him now. Walking downstage, he says: "In the beginning, all I knew was the stage. All I understood was this place. All I knew were lines from plays and jokes made from bodies. The world around me was old, cold, and filled with promises of guns and betrayal. I never really understood what happened outside, past the hall, past the doors into the streets. When I was a boy, I began to wonder if the entire world was a theater. Were the people playing at being powerful? Were other countries as closed as my own? Then, she died, yes, you are right, Consuela died. The architecture of my family collapsed. The anchor to life shifted. It always seems this way, now, and after she died, that I am searching for her voice, and I am searching for the structure…women, they hold the canvas up, and I paint on it–yet I am still looking. We need women in the theater because women can handle the unending story, the story of families collapsing…the story of history ripping itself in half…"

Seemingly forgetting what he was saying, Ducu looks at his hands, pivots towards the ghosts. "How was that?"

"Well", says Molière. "That was very…"

"Sentimental", Ciulei says.

"At least he is trying", Madame Bulandra says. She is now on the stage and stands behind Ciulei, her hands on his shoulders. "I think we failed him."

Ducu, frustrated, puts his hands on his hips. "Really, there is no pleasing you all! I put my heart into that. I really did! Even now you are editing me!"

Before the ghosts have the opportunity to respond, a small man is standing by the downstage exit door pops his head in. His small round glasses cling to his nose, his small bowtie is neat and matches his fitted suit. Surprised to see the theater filled with people, he stutters first and then asks, "Have I come to the wrong place? I'm so very sorry…oh…I seem to have lost my apartment."

At this, Molière, frustrated but feigning compassion, says, "Mikhail, my dear, you have come to the wrong place again."

Ducu sits up straight, and shocked, says to Ciulei, "No! But, it's…"

Ciulei nods as though he's seen it all, and sighs, "Bulgakov. Yes. Poor man is always losing his apartment."

At this, Ducu, turning back to look at Bulgakov, crosses his legs, and remains mute.

"Oh, Jean-Baptiste, you are always so kind…" Bulgakov sighs.

"Mikhail, it is always nice to see you, though, my dear, you seem to forget, your theater, The Moscow Art Theater is…" Molière stands, points upstage as though exhausted by the directions that are needed. "Up the hall, past the pool and forward, where it always is, and to the right your apartment stands waiting for you."

"Kind as always, Jean-Baptiste. That apartment, I'm never sure where it has gone. And I don't seem to be able to get anywhere on time." Bulgakov is now speaking to Ducu. "You know what I mean? And I think I am disappearing again."

At this, Ducu, slightly awestruck, stands. Looking at Bulgakov, he says, "Phillip Philipovich!'

"What? No. I am not–"

"No, I mean, I love Philip Philiovich", Ducu says.

"Ah! *A Dog's Heart*. Yes, yes, that, my dear boy was a long time ago…but not to be forgotten." Bulgakov looks down at his hands and back at Ducu. "Unlike me. You see, I'm being forgotten again."

Ducu and Ciulei cross themselves three times as they watch Bulgakov fading into nothing before them. Ducu, struck by the disappearance, howls: "'Ooow-ow-ooow-owow! Oh, look at me, I'm dying!'"

Bulgakov, nearly forgotten and fading, reaches a hand towards Ducu, and says, "Ah, yes, great first line. I really could write!" And with that, he is gone, poof, like vapor, leaving the witnesses in thrall and slightly sad.

"Ooow-ow-ooow-owow!" howls Ducu, creating vibrations in the theater. Everyone pauses and the theater feels very empty.

Time passes.

"Well", Ciulei says into the silence. "I for one am in the mood for some Beckett."

The hall is quiet again. Ducu lights a cigarette. "You know what? I never directed any Beckett plays."

"No? Why not?" Ciulei says.

"I think I got lost." Ducu shrugs, and drags the cigarette in one, long, languorous breath. The lights shift, the time changes, and he sits in shadow. "Did you know Beckett died on December 22, 1989? He died and then the world changed."

"Yes. That is true", Ciulei says, his chair now seeming to float.

"Perhaps he started the revolution in '89? I mean, why not, he may have asked politely and God granted him one last wish? Can we ask him?" Ducu pleads.

"Oh! No. Beckett is still very private, no one ever sees him. He's tucked away with his words and plays chess all day. No, leave him alone, Ducu. Some things are meant to be a mystery."

A sound of wind gathers in the hall. More trees drop down on winches. Newspapers, crumpled and old, blow across the stage. A small, unsightly tree appears in the hands of a stagehand and is set center stage. Ducu looks around at the wasteland, "Forgive me, but are you sure we can't talk to Beckett?"

"Did you not listen?!" Molière scolds. "We do not bother him unless–"

"Yes, but it seems we are in his scene?" Ducu quips.

"So? We *do not* bother him." Molière takes out a flask and has a drink.

"What do you have there?" Ducu says.

"You're off the sauce. Come on now", Ciulei says.

"Just a sip!" Ducu begs.

"One sip is too much, my dear", Madame Bulandra says.

"But we seem to be waiting. I mean, if not for Beckett, then for what? Come on. Just a little nip since we are waiting for nothing." Ducu stretches his hands toward the flask. Standing, he cups his hands over his mouth and bellows, "Someone get me a fucking drink!"

"No! Ducu, you've been dry for a while", Ciulei says, "Come now. Just–"

"Get me a drink! I'm thirsty and there's nothing here but time. What are we waiting for? I can't even remember why I am here!" Ducu stands, walks to the dead tree, shakes it hard. "And, what *is* this? I mean, is it a metaphor or just a dead tree?! What the fuck! Who is directing this god-forsaken play?!"

Just then, the voices of women explode into the air. They are chanting. They are loud! The women, like a chorus, emerge stage right with banners lofted high. They gather upstage and cup their hands over their mouths as they yell. Their clothing is ripped, ragged, almost falling off. We can't hear what they are saying, but furious, they raise their fists into the air, the banners now clear: "Stop Saying This Is

Nothing!" "Just Because You Don't Have a Life Doesn't Mean WE Care!" And "Stop Making Plays All About You!"

"What is this?" Ducu shouts, looking around interested and confused.

"I told you!" Madame Bulandra says, joining the women upstage. "You should have listened to me, Ducu. You should have invited women in sooner." The women hand Madame Bulandra a banner that reads, "*Really*, We've Heard Enough From You!"

"I have always wanted to join a movement!" Madame Bulandra says, happy in the company of the women.

Out from the back of the crowd, a small woman in black with the handprints of children imprinted on her skirts emerges to the front. She holds up her hands for silence and in a thick New York accent states, "We, the Union of the Silenced and Annoyed are here to address the inequities…"

"Who are you, Madame?" Ducu says.

"Don't sweet talk me!" The woman barks. "I'm not some sucker who'll fall for those eyes or those lips! No sir, I will not!"

"Okay!" Ducu puts up his hands as though before a gun. "Who are you?"

"I am Emma Goldman! I represent the Union and we are here to make some changes at the last minute!" The women cheer!

"Goldman? But you are an anarchist union organizer! And…*an American*!" Molière wails, plunging his face into his hands.

"Damn right! You people are a fuckin' mess! I've been brought in to organize this…this…what is *this*?" she demands, waving her hand at the stage.

"A theater?" Ducu says, smiling, glad for the help.

"Right! Well, it's a dump. A mess! A pile of bones with no vision for the future. And we are tired of it! Tired of all the blah, blah, blah and the lousy management and the…" Goldman takes out a tiny notebook, flips through the pages reading her notes. She pushes her small finger against the pages, "It says it here! We are tired of the way you are lost! We're tired of men being lost, and tired of you saying there is no here here. Because *we* are here. Got it!?" The women cheer louder!

"What are your terms?" Molière demands, now standing, gripping his flask.

"We demand immediate action! We want you to stop hoarding the stage, stop telling us who we are, stop…*doing so much Molière*!" she says, triumphantly.

Molière stands and gasps. Grabs his left arm. Then, falls down.

Everyone stops and looks at him on the floor.

The wind rushes through the theater, up the walls, and around the bodies of the dead.

"Can he die?" Ducu asks Goldman.

"In theory. Yes. But,*everything* is theoretical these days."

"You see. You would miss me!" Molière says from the floor, his body perfectly still. "I am not even dead a minute and you are talking about me!"

The women groan and in unison yell, "*It's not all about you*!"

At this, Ducu laughs. He throws his hands in the air, and cries, "Nothing changes!"

"Victory!" Goldman declares. "Finally, we have a breakthrough. Nothing changes and we want something to change. So, consider our demands! We have to leave now, the Living Theater is waiting for us in the streets!"

And with this, the chorus of forgotten women, theater artists of all kinds, ripped and torn memories from theater walls and halls and street corners, collectively pull out new banners that read "Paradise Is Not Lost!" and hoist them into the air, chanting in unison, "Get over yourself! Get over yourself!" And, they leave stage left.

Only Madame Bulandra remains from the crowd of women. She stands watching them depart as she waves. "Ah! Now I have really lived!" She wipes her eyes, tenderly.

Molière jumps to his feet, turns towards the cameras, and returns to hosting the show. "Ladies and gentlemen, I have been a clown all my life. I've tried as best I can…" Molière turns to Ciulei and begs, "What am I talking about?"

"Sir, you have been rendered irrelevant. I suggest you stop and collect yourself." Ciulei stands, moves his chair closer to Ducu, and whispers, "You see, he's never really been silenced. We know what that's like. We know what it means to be forgotten."

Sighing deeply, Ducu stands, runs to the dead tree, unzips his pants, and pees on the tree, howling like Bulgakov's dog: "Ooow-ow-ooow-owow! Oh, look at me, I'm dying!"

From out of the nowhere, cheers erupt from the audience, "Bravo! Bravo! What a way to go!"

Sitting in the middle of the audience are three ghosts, writers from my childhood, all dead now: Sam Shepard with his cowboy boots on the seat before him, Maria Irene Fornes holding a coffee cup from a Greek diner, and Harry Koutoukas covered head to toe in gold lamé. "Bravo!" they say and whistle like the end of a punk explosion at the club CBGBs.

"Hey!" Sam shouts. "Any of you cowboys have a fresh pack of smokes?"

Ducu checks his pockets, finds a pack, looks at it, kisses it, and throws it to Sam. "Thanks kid!" says Sam, pulling out three cigarettes, handing one each to Irene and Harry like communion. All three light up and suck hard on their smokes, lustily.

Molière, incensed, stands. "Who let all these.... ruffians...these coarse...*Americans* in?"

Laughter erupts amongst the seated ghosts. "I told you! What a charmer, huh?" Harry says about Molière.

"Yeah, this guy", Irene says. "When did you sell out and move to television?!"

"Sell out?" Molière says, hurt.

"Yeah, you! Sellout! You think you have what it takes to interview Ducu? Huh?" Harry barks. Molière stands, pulls his hair, and sits again.

"Harry?" Ducu says. "Is that you?"

"Hey, baby, how are you darling?" Harry purrs.

"Confused, sweetheart." Ducu says. "What do you three want?"

"Same as always", Irene says, her voice calm. "A great show!"

"I would have made something for you..." Ducu stands now, his hands covering eyes. "I'm imagining something loud with lots of ways for the characters to escape!"

"Yes! That sounds wonderful", Sam says, smiling.

Molière stands, cups his mouth, yells to the light board operator, "Hey, play that song! They want a show, play it now!"

The voice of Patti Smith flows through the hall, the blue paint chips at the sounds of her cry. "Jesus died for somebody's sins…but not mine!" The thumping beat of her cries for "G-L-O-R-I-A!" shake the walls.

Sam jumps to his feet, terrified, "No! Patti is not dead! What is this?" Harry and Irene also jump to their feet, to comfort Sam. Harry points at Molière. "You think this is funny? You sick bastard!"

"Oh, I'm the sick bastard! You three are always showing up to interrupt me, judge me, call out your demands!" Molière pouts.

"That's our job, you brat!" Irene barks. "Now, tell him, Patti is not here. Tell him!" Irene says this as she holds Sam's hand. Sam is terrified and shaking.

"I will do no such thing!" Molière screeches.

"What's going on here?" Ducu pleads with Ciulei.

"The *avant-gard*e. They're always fighting with sombody", Ciulei says as Madame Bulandra nods her head in agreement.

"Oh! You call this clown our authority?" Irene says, her hand on her small hip, her dark eyes wild. "Molière, you bastard! Tell him Patti isn't here! She's not dead!"

"I won't!" Molière says, his arms crossed before his chest like an angry child.

"What a hack!" Harry bellows from his seat. "If you don't tell him, Molière, I'm going to call Charles!"

"You wouldn't dare upstage me, Koutoukas!" Molière says, terrified.

"Tell him! Assure him! Patti is alive!" Harry barks.

"I will do no such thing you…you…*bohemians*!" Molière points at the three ghosts, wildly waving his hand.

"Oh, now he's done it." Irene says to Harry. Harry nods with a Cheshire Cat smile.

"Charles!" Harry yells, "Charles! Come out here and shut this hack up!"

The lights change on the stage, and a set piece falls upstage with a huge thunk. The set is painted in bold colors, the images large, the scene a tableaux of an old Parisian salon in a distant past.

"Not fair!" Molière bellows. "Not fair at all!"

Sam, Irene, and Harry applaud and whistle over Molière. They pound their feet as Ducu and Ciulei stand, pulling their seats back. They stand stage right, mouths agape.

A single spotlight lights up a lone figure in a 19th century dress, tight at the waist and flowing out and out, layers of skirts meeting the stage. It is Charles Ludlam, the neck of the dress dangerously low, the hair of his chest peeking out over the fabric.

"No! Not…Camille!" Molière bellows.

"You asked for it!" Irene laughs.

Charles is hit with a second spotlight. He stares up and out over the audience, "Well, how do you do?" he says, pulling up his skirts as he slowly makes his way downstage, lightly touching his face, his thick fingers elegant, leaving pink marks on his cheek. Finishing his steps, he looks up at the balcony. Only the shadows of my dead are sitting in the seats. Charles steps forward and Ducu stands, points at the lights, and like a magician shifts the lighting to seep behind Charles, who's dazzling.

"Darlings! Ladies and germs! What's the point to being dead if you can't have the last act all to yourself? Right, my darlings?" Sam, Irene, and Harry hoot and stomp their feet. "What's left for us dead?" Charles continues. "Memories? And, who remembers us? When we were always the forgotten ones? Molière, what do you have to say for yourself?"

Molière staggering up from his chair tries to speak but cannot, sits again, takes out his flask, and gulps a shot, and says, "Upstaging me. You're cruel."

Charles laughs, deeply. "Oh, vain even as a phantom! We're all whores for the light. But, I still have something to say…" Sam, Irene, and Harry applaud hard. Emboldened by the support, Charles looks around, walks to the edge of the stage, and takes a breath, the sound of wind rising around him. Ducu stands, leaning against the wall of the theater, up on the stage as Charles gathers himself for one last testament to life. Ducu's face is as lit up as Charles', both enlightened by the moment.

Collecting his skirts, Charles makes his way forward to speak. He opens his mouth and a Tibetan chant bellows out, reverberates for a long time, the sound so powerful Sam, Irene, and Harry dissolve before me, the flicker of them quickly gone.

The seats are all filled with shadows of the dead, all the dead theater people Ducu or I had ever known. The box seats resonate with gongs. Moving center stage, Ducu takes Charles's hand, and they both look out into the theater. "Oh!" Ducu exclaims. "It is true. I am dead."

Smiling sweetly, Charles looks to Ducu and they nod, knowing what to do. Both take a deep bow as the chants of monks cue the lights to fade.

They bow low. They bow long though there is no sound of applause. Charles disappears into the floorboards of the stage. Ducu looks out into the theater, "Yes!" he cries. "Yes, I am dead!"

I am suddenly standing on the stage, furious. I have the camera down by my leg, the sounds of branches seemingly rubbing against me. "Will we ever get to the truth with you?!" I demand, the ghosts aghast. "Can we just get a clear answer? How did you die? What will happen next?"

Ducu pulls my ears, lightly. He smells my hair. He smiles *that* smile, "Don't be mad, baby. Watch this…"

The ceiling above the stage opens up. The sound is massive as it pulls away, revealing the night sky. Ducu walks center stage. Looking up, he laughs, and looks at all of us on the stage, "I think I'll leave now."

A Klezmer band begins to play and Ducu laughs. All the lights in the sky and all the stars point towards the stage. We look up at the gleaming, clear night sky. Then, ropes drop. Acrobats shimmy halfway down the ropes and stop to spin, their hair loose, their costumes covered in stars.

"Well! That is a way to go", Molière says, turning to the cameras. "Here, on the stage of the

Bulandra, not to be shown up by his past, we end this evening with a live performance."

Molière's voice dissipates as the klezmer's oom-pah-pah fills the hall. The acrobats continue to spin. The music picks up. Ducu stands in the middle of the stage, his arms reaching up and up, until a red rope drops, hard before him. Looking up, he smiles seeing a red-masked woman hanging upside down. Her nose looks familiar. Her eyes are filled with tears. Her black hair, close-cropped, is loose and elegant. "Come, darling…" she whispers from above.

"Yes", he says, and starts to climb the rope towards her. Now, the sky-bound circus is singing along with the band, so loudly it's hard to hear anything else. Ducu rises, taking his time as he looks around the hall. He bends back towards me and tells me something.

"What?" I yell.

He leans back toward me again, I cannot hear. Moving closer to the rope, I look up, directly into his eyes.

"Find Maria, baby!" he yells, reaching for the woman's hand. Her grasp is strong as she pulls him towards the infinite in order to go up and up because heaven is a theater. She pulls him up and up, and I hear him yell back at me, "And, wake up, love. Wake up."

Epilogue

"Wake up, love. Wake up", Lars said, his hand soft on my shoulder. "Your phone is ringing."

I pulled myself up. It was cold and the fog was outside the window. I looked at the phone. The call was from Romania. Thinking it might be Anya, I panicked. Then, I saw it: a text from Maria.

She wanted to talk on the phone. "Can we speak now?" I wrote back. The phone rang and I collected myself, threw on a sweater, and pulled myself away to the living room.

Her words woke me from the entire nightmare. When I heard her, I knew her. When she spoke, I believed her. I told her everything quickly, as though I might not survive.

"Why didn't you reach out to me?" she said. "This person is crazy!"

"Was she with Ducu?"

"No!"

"I'm sorry, Maria, I should have reached out to you."

"I'm sorry! I should have reached out to *you*. But, why didn't you?"

"I was ashamed."

"Of what?"

"How in the past I hurt you."

There was a long silence, the physical distance between us reminding me of all the years I had thought of her. Knew how deeply Ducu loved her. I felt her breathing on the other end and prayed to God she was so very real. Smiling in the silence, I felt forgiven. I hoped she felt respected. The long pain of the past cut open like a pear, and, suddenly, we had each other.

I asked, finally, "Is Anton safe and well?"

"Of course, he is fine."

"But, what happened to Ducu? Where are his books?"

"Oh, sweetheart", she said, and then she told me all of it: how he'd died in the hospital directly at noon, where the books had gone, where the CD's of music live, how his cats were, and then she sent pictures of their small faces as they rested in the sun sitting on her floor. Yes, he had been isolated. Yes, he was not alone when he died. Yes, he left a mess.

Yes, he had admitted it all: how the world was not a theater and that confused him–all this he'd admitted to her. Yes, he'd grown aware he had been made a fool, many times, in many ways, but still laughed. Yes, he was gone now. She said how he had seemed to float away–that he was not reachable in the end, that he had pushed everyone off as though he were headed for a new country. Oh god, yes, he was a mystery, but he was *our* mystery.

I saw his favorite red.

I saw his hands resting in his grave.

I heard the sound of the theater, his theater, blue with feelings and the past.

He is gone, and we remain, and the path to this moment is filled with suspicions and lies, countries returning to old fears, artists afraid again and journalists silenced, the path of freedom obscured by politicians making money off our pain–all of this is true, we are all in the Con, we are all writing or buying some form of the narrative, we are all trying to find home, one safe with people who know us, see us, and believe we are telling the truth.

And what of us? The "us" that is me and Maria? We are each other's legacy. We loved him. And we lost him–in life and in death. We keep searching the spaces of theaters for him. We keep remembering the smell of him in the world. We share the ghost of him, the body he once had -- the art he made.

This phantom love, this is what holds me up in a world collapsing. And it is Maria who might save me from the vortex, the mess I have made.

Maria and I write each other every morning. We send each other pictures of the sea or snow. We plan to meet in Budapest or Rome to walk and re-member. We send each other love and luck. Because that's the truth of it, what we all want: love, to reach toward it, reaching and reaching for it past the broken, craven, honest edges

(*of death.)*

Acknowledgments

I wish to thank the remarkable friends who stood by me during this strange experience and supported me during the iterations of writing this book—Steve Bottoms, Teadora-Campineanu, Marina Draghici, Lisa Gorlitsky, Cristina Modreanu, Bill Oram, Jendi Reiter, Micela Sidor and Janis Nakano Spivack.

I must also thank the friends who are family for believing in me and this project, and whose strength and clarity support me in every way. A deep thank you to Cate Riegner, Ilaria Bulgari and Jan Boyer, Domitilla Sartogo and Paulo von Vocano, Emily Stone, Lance McCready, September Williams and of course, my parents, Lawrence and Margaret Kornfeld.

I am indebted to the beautiful editing, daring and approach of Sally Arteseros—all the words I have for her exist in every space and comma in this book. More thanks go to John Madera for his brilliant editing and launch support. My deepest thanks go to Costel Postolache, publisher of Editura Integral, for his belief in this project and for the inspired direction he gave me at a critical juncture in the development of the manuscript—"Ghosts! More Ghosts", he said.

I must acknowledge my son, Luca, whose energy and heart are always my muse. And, to Arne, as always and forever, who waited with love and led me through.

And to Maria Miu for her generosity of heart and strength, her demand I express my truth, her reading of each version of the book, her vision for the design of the book covers, and finally, her friendship.

About the book

Sarah Kornfeld's *The True* is a gorgeously written twenty-first century postmodern literary work convincing us that we only truly know where we are when on the wrong side of the looking glass. Passion, politics, lust, and theater drag us between the surreal and the real, on both sides of the Atlantic. This is a "now" age romance-political thriller. Kornfeld forces us to weigh what we hate against love, or at least find the middle ground between them, in order to fully live.

September Williams, MD, Filmmaker,
Author of the *Chasing Mercury Toxic Trilogy*

Storytelling is a contract of trust between speaker and listener–the promise that the suspension of disbelief will be rewarded with deeper truths encoded in fiction. But "in this time of virtual lives", Kornfeld warns, such trust is easier to manipulate than ever, and the magic of theater degenerates into propaganda and psychosis. (…)

Kornfeld is humbled to discover how anyone, regardless of political beliefs or intellectual sophistication, can cling to wishful thinking as a defense against personal and historical trauma.

THE TRUE is a funny, tragic, essential cautionary tale for our post-truth era.

Jendi Reiter,
Author of *An Incomplete List of My Wishes: Stories*

Intimate, funny and page-turning, *The True* simultaneously expresses the ways in which we are haunted by memory and the ways we continue to con ourselves. What starts out as a love story that transcends time becomes a paean to the world of theater set against the backdrop of the AIDS crisis and crumbling Romania. This book has everything: romance, Ceaușescu, Diana Ross. Interwoven throughout, the terror and pathos of being Jewish in Europe. The long tail of the Holocaust, the (c)overt antisemitism that still comprises common parlance. What does it mean to be a Jew searching for a Jew? What is Jewish identity? What is identity? Kornfeld's lucid prose cuts close to the heart and lends an immediacy to the whole crazy story as we watch everything unravel. The downward spiral has such a tentacular pull. I couldn't put the book down!

Emily Stone, Author of *Did Jew Know*

The True: A Trilogy of Ghosts evocatively limns the insubstantiality of the "they": the vestiges of the self and multitude in the virtual realm; the hauntings of the living and the dead, of the past, present, and future, of the real versus the unreal; the liminality of lyings to oneself, of identity creation and fraud in many iterations. Here, the present is as mysterious as the future is uncertain, the past interrogatively tincturing everything. Memoir, mystery, and double-Künstlerroman collide and blur as the text deeply engages Romanian political and social histories and their intertwinings, moreover time and timing, the art of creation, the reel and unreal of real life, of people as shadows, shadows as people.

Evocatively navigating readers within, through, and past the "frozen falseness" of unfamiliar places and spaces, gardens that "smell of death", the desert of desertion, the "wet loss of time", the "broken, craven, honest edges (of death)", you paint portraits of a troubled confidence woman, and a (mis)leading man from "everywhere", you, like him, listening to and ventriloquizing voices within and without. Have I mentioned the engaging intertextuality (Bulgakov, Shakespeare, and Molière), and your marvelous miniatures of cities (Bucharest, New York City, and San Francisco)? "We were the madness", "death can make you cleave to life", "What if nothing was real?" you knowingly write.

About the book

Matryoshka doll or *mise enabîme* or both, *The True: A Trilogy of Ghosts* is a haunting, and, like the best hauntings, is as moving as it is harrowing.

John Madera, Editor, *Big Other*

The True is a compelling, troubling, and painfully honest story about the world we live in now–a world of fake news and alternative facts in which we believe what we want to believe and ignore or deny those nagging voices that tell us otherwise. It's also a story about theatre–that most ancient art of dissembling; a world of artifice in which nothing is quite what it seems, but where deception is deployed in search of profound truths. And it is also a story about Romania, and about the twisted western view of that troubled eastern nation. Our narrator travels there in search of her undead lover, with Bucharest standing in for Transylvania, and bloodsuckers lurking at every turn. But in Kornfeld's deftly woven tale, there is sympathy even for the devil. *The True* lures the reader in with its dark poetry, and then refuses to let us go.

Stephen Scott-Bottoms

Professor of Contemporary Theatre and Performance

Martin Harris Centre for Music and Drama

University of Manchester

About the author

Sarah Kornfeld is an American writer born and raised in the experimental theater of New York City, where she performed with The Bread and Puppet Theater, Judson Poets Theater, and The Ridiculous Theatrical Company. She is a graduate of Sarah Lawrence College and received professional training at The Royal Court Theater in London. Her play, THE LOVEDEATH OF CLOWNS was produced at the Theater For The New City in New York. Her debut novel, WHAT STELLA SEES was published by Cove International Publishers in 2018 and received high praise in the United States and the United Kingdom. She is a proud member of the National Writers Union, and lives by the sea in the Bay Area of California.

INTEGRAL PUBLISHERS
eintegral.ro
game of knowledge